D1278913

Enrichment Series
The Ginn Basic Readers
by David H. Russell and Others

Along *Story* *Trails*

David H. Russell

Doris Gates

Louise Markert

Ginn and Company

Boston	New York	Chicago	Atlanta
Dallas	Palo Alto	Toronto	

Acknowledgments

Grateful acknowledgment is made to the following authors and publishers for permission to use and adapt copyrighted materials:

Abingdon Press for "The Wreck," adapted from ISLAND SUMMER, by Hazel Wilson. © Copyright 1949 by Pierce and Smith; used with permission of Abingdon Press, Publishers.

Brandt & Brandt for "Johnny Appleseed," by Rosemary Carr Benét, from A BOOK OF AMERICANS, by Rosemary and Stephen Vincent Benét, Holt, Rinehart and Winston, Inc., Copyright, 1933, by Rosemary and Stephen Vincent Benét, Copyright renewed, 1961, by Rosemary Carr Benét. Reprinted by permission of Brandt & Brandt.

Doubleday & Company, Inc., for "The Wonderful Adventure of Nils," from the book THE WONDERFUL ADVENTURES OF NILS, by Selma Lagerlöf, copyright © 1907 by Doubleday & Company, Inc. For "Rikki-tikki-tavi," from THE JUNGLE BOOK, by Rudyard Kipling, reprinted by permission of Mrs. George Bambridge and Doubleday & Company, Inc.

E. P. Dutton & Co., Inc., for "It Is Raining," from ANOTHER HERE AND NOW STORY BOOK, by Lucy Sprague Mitchell. Copyright, 1937, by E. P. Dutton & Co., Inc. Reprinted by permission of the publishers.

Harcourt, Brace and World, Inc. for "Flan Makes Good," adapted from WILDERNESS JOURNEY, copyright, 1953, by William O. Steele. Used by permission of Harcourt, Brace & World, Inc. For "Buffalo Dusk," from SMOKE AND STEEL, by Carl Sandburg, copyright, 1920, by Harcourt, Brace & World, Inc.; copyright, 1948, by Carl Sandburg. Reprinted by permission of the publishers. For the first stanza only of "The Rum Tum Tugger," in OLD POSSUM'S BOOK OF PRACTICAL CATS,

5

Mrs. George Bambridge for permission to reprint "Rikki-tikki-tavi," from The Jungle Book, by Rudyard Kipling.

Central News Agency, Ltd., Johannesburg, South Africa, for "Animals at Home," an adaptation of "Fun on the Veld," from Look Out for the Ostriches, by Jan Juta, published by Alfred A. Knopf, Inc.

Child Life Magazine for "A Valentine," by Eleanor Hammond, originally published in *Child Life Magazine*, February, 1927.

Padraic Colum for "Orpheus and Eurydice," from Orpheus: Myths of the World by Padraic Colum, published by The Macmillan Company, Copyright © 1930. Used by permission of the author.

J. M. Dent & Sons, Ltd., Publishers, of London, for "The Wonderful Adventure of Nils," from The Wonderful Adventures of Nils, by Selma Lagerlöf, copyright © 1907 by Doubleday & Company, Inc.

Eleanor Hammond Doar for the poem "A Valentine," by Eleanor Hammond, from the February, 1927, issue of *Child Life Magazine*.

Dodd, Mead & Company for "Beowulf's Fight with Grendel," by Hamilton W. Mabie. Reprinted and adapted by permission of Dodd, Mead & Company.

Faber and Faber Ltd., of London, for the first stanza of "The Rum Tum Tugger," from Old Possum's Book of Practical Cats, by T. S. Eliot, copyright 1939 by Faber and Faber Ltd.

Holiday House for "Hunting the Haunt Fox," adapted from Haunt Fox by Jim Kjelgaard. Used with permission of the publisher.

The Horn Book, Inc. for permission to reprint "House on the Hill," by Nora S. Unwin, from the February, 1961, *The Horn Book Magazine*.

Houghton Mifflin Company for "Robinson Crusoe's Story," by Charles Edward Carryl from 100 Poems about People, selected by Elinor Parker, copyright 1955.

Mrs. Josephine Lofting for "Tommy Stubbins Meets Doctor Dolittle," from The Voyages of Doctor Dolittle, by Hugh Lofting, and for the illustrations by Hugh Lofting which accompany the excerpt from the book, copyright 1948 by Josephine Lofting.

Lutterworth Press, London, for permission to reprint "Winter Days" and "Wolves on Silver Lake," from By the Shores of Silver Lake, by Laura Ingalls Wilder. Copyright 1939 by Harper & Brothers.

McClelland and Stewart Limited, Toronto, for permission to use an adaptation of "Watchers of the Camp-Fire," from Kindred of the Wild, by Charles G. D. Roberts.

The Macmillan Company of Canada, and Messrs. Macmillan & Co., Ltd., for permission to reprint "Rikki-tikki-tavi," from The Jungle Book, by Rudyard Kipling.

Harold Matson Company for "The River Crossing," adapted from Old Ramon, by Jack Schaefer, published 1960 by Houghton Mifflin Company, Boston.

New Directions for "Poem," from The Collected Earlier Poems of William Carlos Williams. Copyright 1938, 1951, by William Carlos Williams. Reprinted by permission of New Directions, New York, Publishers.

Norman Holmes Pearson for permission to reprint the poem, "Storm," from Sea Garden, by Hilda Doolittle Aldington, copyright 1924. Reprinted by permission of Norman Holmes Pearson, owner of the copyright.

Laurence Pollinger Limited, authors' agents, London, for permission to reprint "The Pasture," by Robert Frost, from The Complete Poems of Robert Frost, by Robert Frost. Publishers: Messrs. Jonathan Cape, Ltd., of London, England. Proprietors: Messrs. Holt, Rinehart & Winston, Inc., New York.

Rand McNally & Company for the adaptation of "King of the Wind," from King of the Wind, by Marguerite Henry. Copyright 1948 by Rand McNally & Company, publishers.

Miss Rosalind Richards and Rand McNally & Company for permission to reprint the poem "Antonio," by Laura E. Richards, from *Child Life Magazine*, copyright 1936 by Rand McNally & Company.

Mrs. Maria Ruckel for permission to reprint the poem "The Pirate Don Durk of Dowdee," by Mildred Plew Meigs published in *Child Life Magazine*, March, 1923.

The Society of Authors for "All But Blind," from COLLECTED POEMS 1901–1918 by Walter de la Mare, and for "I Saw Three Witches," from POEMS FOR CHILDREN by Walter de la Mare, 1930. Permission has been granted by The Literary Trustees of Walter de la Mare and The Society of Authors as their representative.

Mrs. Martha A. Tippett for permission to reprint the poem "George Washington," by James S. Tippett.

The Viking Press, Inc. for "The Escape," adapted from A BRIDLE FOR PEGASUS, by Katherine B. Shippen. Copyright 1951 by Katherine B. Shippen. Reprinted by permission of the Viking Press, Inc.

A. P. Watt & Son, and Mrs. George Bambridge, for permission to reprint "Rikki-tikki-tavi," from THE JUNGLE BOOK, by Rudyard Kipling.

Yale University Press for "The Boy Pu-nia and the King of the Sharks," adapted from Padraic Colum's LEGENDS OF HAWAII.

Illustrations by Tom Cooke, Denver Gillen, David Jonas, Gordon Laite, Susan Perl, Jo Polseno, Charlotte Purrington, Ralph Ricketts, Brian Wildsmith.

Contents

Courage and Daring

		PAGE
Books—Poem	Eleanor Farjeon	12
Flan Makes Good	William O. Steele	14
Spurs for Antonia	Katherine Wigmore Eyre	26
A Dog of the Alps	Alice Gall and Fleming Crew	36
The Escape	Katherine B. Shippen	44
The Heart That Dares—Poem	Author Unknown	51
The Wreck	Hazel Wilson	52
The Attack	Elizabeth Coatsworth	64
A Song of Greatness—Poem	A Chippewa Indian Song Transcribed by Mary Austin	78

Animals All

Hunting the Haunt Fox	Jim Kjelgaard	80
Night of Wind—Poem	Frances Frost	93
March of Death	Sigmund A. Lavine	94
All But Blind—Poem	Walter de la Mare	101
Watchers of the Campfire	Charles G. D. Roberts	102
Buffalo Dusk—Poem	Carl Sandburg	111

		PAGE
The River Crossing	*Jack Schaefer*	112
Animals at Home	*Jan Juta*	124
The Hippopotamus—POEM	*Georgia Roberts Durston*	134

Friends in Books

King of the Wind	*Marguerite Henry*	136
The Blood Horse—POEM	*Barry Cornwall*	147
Tommy Stubbins Meets Doctor Dolittle	*Hugh Lofting*	148
Winter Days	*Laura Ingalls Wilder*	158
Billy Minds the Baby	*Marion Holland*	168
The Wonderful Adventure of Nils	*Selma Lagerlöf*	182
A Mad Tea-Party	*Lewis Carroll*	194
Robinson Crusoe's Story—POEM	*Charles Edward Carryl*	207

Great Stories

The Boy Pu-nia and the King of the Sharks	*Padraic Colum*	210
Orpheus and Eurydice	*Padraic Colum*	218
Orpheus with His Lute—POEM	*William Shakespeare*	225
Beowulf's Fight with Grendel	*Hamilton W. Mabie*	226
The Making of the Hammer	*A Norse Myth*	240
The Pied Piper—PLAY	*Fan Kissen*	250
The Good Joan—POEM	*Lizette Woodworth Reese*	268
Chanticleer and the Fox	*Adapted by Barbara Cooney from The Canterbury Tales by Geoffrey Chaucer*	270
The Fox—POEM	*Old Rhyme*	277

9

Singing Words

		PAGE
Poems	*Hilda Conkling*	280

Sounds in Words

The Rum Tum Tugger	*T. S. Eliot*	281
Antonio	*Laura E. Richards*	282
House on the Hill	*Nora S. Unwin*	283
The Mysterious Cat	*Vachel Lindsay*	284

Some Poems Tell Stories

Johnny Appleseed	*Rosemary and Stephen Vincent Benét*	285
The Raggle, Taggle Gypsies	*Old Folk Song*	288
The Pirate Don Durk of Dowdee	*Mildred Plew Meigs*	290
Meg Merrilies	*John Keats*	292

Poems About Things Around You

Rain Sizes	*John Ciardi*	294
City Lights	*Rachel Field*	295
It Is Raining	*Lucy Sprague Mitchell*	296
Dandelions	*Frances Frost*	298
The Pasture	*Robert Frost*	298

Poems Without Rhyme

Poem	*William Carlos Williams*	299
Storm	*Hilda Doolittle Aldington*	300
Snow-Capped Mountain	*Hilda Conkling*	301
The Winter Is Past	*The Song of Songs*	301

Poems for Special Days

		PAGE
Columbus	Annette Wynne	302
I Saw Three Witches	Walter de la Mare	304
Christmas Hearth Rhyme	Old English	306
My Valentine	Robert Louis Stevenson	307
A Valentine	Eleanor Hammond	307
George Washington	James S. Tippett	308
Written in March	William Wordsworth	310

The Long Story

Rikki-tikki-tavi	Rudyard Kipling	312
Some Books to Read		338
Your Glossary		339

Books

What worlds of wonder are our books!
As one opens them and looks,
New ideas and people rise
In our fancies and our eyes.

The room we sit in melts away,
And we find ourselves at play
With someone who, before the end,
May become our chosen friend.

Or we sail along the page
To some other land or age.
Here's our body in the chair,
But our mind is over *there*.

Each book is a magic box
Which with a touch a child unlocks.
In between their outside covers
Books hold all things for their lovers.

Eleanor Farjeon

Courage and Daring

Flan Makes Good

IT WAS THE HOTTEST DAY Flan could remember. He
struggled along the trail, up and down the rolling hills, with
his shirt clinging to his back. He was grateful for every patch
of shade and cool stream they came to. The horses too
lingered at the springs, their hides dark with sweat.

"Smells like rain," said Mr. Green. "We'd ought to make
it to Cumberland Gap by night." He studied the sky where
great cloud banks were gathering. "We'll get wet afore we
get there, I reckon, but I won't mind. I'm dry as the old well
right now."

They walked on steadily. To their right the long blue line
of the Cumberland Mountains stayed in sight but came no
closer. Mr. Green quickened his pace, and Flan set his teeth
and forced his legs to move faster.

For nearly two weeks Flan and Mr. Green had been going up hills and down, and wading creeks, on their way to the French Salt Lick. Mr. Green went first with his long rifle and leading the two horses, both of which carried a heavy load of powder. This was the year 1782, Indians were on the warpath again, and the blockhouse at the French Salt Lick was short of powder.

Flan's folks were already at the blockhouse. He had been forced to remain behind when they had taken the trail. Flan was puny and small for his age. He couldn't shoot, he couldn't hunt, he didn't know how to skin a deer. He wasn't good for much of anything because he always had been puny. So he stayed behind with Uncle Henry until he got over the shakes. And then Mr. Green, the Long Hunter and Indian fighter, had come along and agreed to take him to the French Salt Lick where he could be with his folks again.

Flan admired Mr. Green. He could shoot a rifle and hit the mark every time. He was a fine woodsman and could read a trail the way Flan could read a book. Flan wished he could be like Mr. Green and not a puny good-for-nothing. It was even hard for him to keep up with the Long Hunter, but Flan never complained. He knew Mr. Green was traveling more slowly than he would by himself. He knew the people at the Lick were waiting anxiously for the powder. So he tried bravely to keep his legs moving as fast as he could.

As night fell, they came to the top of a hill. The wind roared through the valley below them. Just behind them a great branch broke from a hickory tree and fell to the ground. Flan jumped, thinking it might be Indians. He knew he was too tired to run.

The Cumberland Mountains loomed right overhead now, and dark thunderheads piled up behind them. A spattering of rain fell, and a flash of lightning split the sky.

"It ain't much further to the Gap, now," Mr. Green shouted over the wind. "There's a cave there I know of. We can sleep dry in it."

Flan hoped it wasn't far. It was so dark he could hardly see to walk. Then the storm was on them, pounding against the side of the mountain like horses' hoofs. The rain stung his eyes, and he stumbled forward, blinded, frightened, and half-drowned.

Mr. Green guided him by the shoulder, and they stumbled on. Flan could hear his sobbing breath, and his chest felt as if it were splitting for lack of air. Then in the next lightning flash he could see the mouth of a cave in front of them.

"Here," shouted the Long Hunter. "Hold these horses, Flan, while I get the powder in the cave."

It was all Flan could do to hold them. In the flashes of lightning he could see the foam on their great mouths. He had thought the horses were his friends, but now he scarcely recognized them in these huge wild beasts that reared and whinnied and jerked at the reins.

In a moment Mr. Green took the thongs from his hand. "I'll tie 'em over yonder," he shouted, nodding to a place nearby. Flan didn't wait to watch but scooted into the cave. It was so low he had to bend forward to keep from bumping his head.

Mr. Green came stumbling in, all bent over, a few minutes later.

"I tied the horses good," he announced. "All this thunder and lightning is liable to send them both straight over to Chickasaw country. We don't want to have to spend tomorrow looking for 'em. Not but what the critters wouldn't break a leg getting down this mountain in the rain."

Mr. Green checked his rifle, putting fresh powder in the pan. Then Flan watched as he examined the floor of the cave. All at once he straightened up.

"Some friends left us a fire in here," he said. "It was neighborly of 'em, but they had no call to throw a broken arrowhead down for us to find."

Indians! Flan began to shiver in earnest and crept closer to the fire.

"If they aim to come back and use this fire tonight, I aim to know about it before they get here," Mr. Green said as he left the cave.

After Mr. Green had gone, Flan wished he had gone with him. Suppose the Indians did come back and found him here alone! He'd be scalped for sure. He hoped Mr. Green would come back soon.

Finally he went to the front of the cave and crouched there, looking out into the night. The rain had slackened a good bit, but the lightning was dazzling bright, and the thunder rolled among the hills. He could see the dark shapes of the horses.

Suddenly there was a terrible blazing light all around him, a hissing, crackling sound, and then such a roar of thunder that it seemed to fling him back into the cave. He pressed himself against the rocks and peered out. The lightning had struck a tree, a dead pine tree standing not twenty yards from the entrance to the cave. In spite of the heavy rain it was burning fiercely.

And then in the light from the burning tree Flan saw the two horses, Meg and Brownie. Terror-stricken, the poor beasts reared and plunged, jerking at the thongs that held them. Fiery splinters from the burning tree fell around them and on them. They screamed and lashed out with their hoofs as they tried desperately to get away.

Flan knew in an instant that someone would have to loose the horses. If the lightning-fired tree didn't fall on them and burn them, they'd kill each other rearing and fighting that way.

"Mr. Green!" he yelled. "Mr. Green!"

But he knew Mr. Green couldn't hear, nor get to the horses in time if he heard. The horses would be killed, and the powder they'd brought this long way would never reach the people waiting at the Lick.

With a despairing cry Flan ran toward the plunging, maddened horses.

He kept his eyes on Meg as he ran. She was the nearest. He would free her first. He circled wide to avoid the plunging hoofs, slipping and stumbling over the rocks. Once a branch, heavy with rain, slapped him across the face and sent him sprawling among the wet underbrush.

One of the horses screamed.

"I'm a-coming, Meg," he panted, struggling on. His wet buckskins made him slow and awkward.

Finally he reached the spot where Meg was tied. Just beyond, the fire roared and crackled. He put up his arm to shield his face from the heat. In the red glow of the burning tree the horses looked as big as mountains. Their lips were pulled back from the great yellow teeth, and their eyes rolled madly. Again and again they reared before him and came plunging back to earth.

Flan began to work at the knot, picking at it with trembling fingers. He couldn't seem to get hold of the wet leather and finally he began to claw desperately at the thong. He wished Mr. Green hadn't tied it so tight, or that Meg wouldn't pull it tighter every time he tried to loosen it.

He glanced up at the flaming tree, towering over him in the blackened sky. It couldn't burn much longer. The top at least was bound to fall in another moment, and they'd all be burned to death. He had to do something quick.

His knife! What a wooden-head he'd been! He snatched out his hunting knife and reached for the leather thong.

There was a sudden sharp crack that made him jump. A branch broke from the burning pine and crashed to the ground. A big flake of blazing wood lit on his hand, and he dropped the knife. Half-sobbing, he crouched to pick it up, snatching among those wicked hoofs and at last seizing it.

He pulled himself up by holding on to Meg's tree. He could feel it tremble as Meg jerked in panic. Her eyes were wild and staring. Foam fell from her lips.

He slashed again at the leather thong. A shower of sparks sent the horses screaming and rearing worse than ever. He hung back for a second, but then he was sawing away at the thong again, standing as far back from the horses as he could.

At last Meg was free. He heard the hard sound of her hoofs on the rocks as she vanished. He turned to Brownie.

The horse was wild with fear. He lashed out at Flan, his big hoofs grazing the tree to which he was tied. Flan couldn't get close enough to cut him loose, and that tree would fall at any moment. Desperately he lunged forward and slashed at the thong where it circled the tree. He cut it cleanly and jumped away. With a terror-filled whinny Brownie sped away.

"Run, Flan! The tree! Run!" Mr. Green's voice from the trail was hoarse. "This way, Flan!"

Flan stood panic-stricken under the flaming tree, trying to decide which way to run. Mr. Green's voice steadied him, and he darted toward it. It seemed like a year of struggling over slippery stones before he felt himself seized and dragged inside the cave.

There was a crash and a moment of wild flaming light, and a million stars seemed to fly through the night. But he was safe. He lay on the floor of the cave panting and gasping until Mr. Green bent over him.

"Are you all right, lad?" he asked anxiously. "You ain't burnt?" he asked as he pulled the boy to his feet.

Flan shook his head. "I ain't hurt," he said finally, though there was a blister as big as a frog on the back of his hand.

They walked back into the room of the cave, and Mr. Green threw some dry sticks on the Indians' left-over fire. It flamed up, and Flan took off his wet clothes and sat wrapped in his blanket beside it.

"I'll get some mud to put on that burn," said Mr. Green.

"You're a brave lad," he announced a moment later as he gently spread the mud on the back of Flan's burned hand. "When I saw the fire and heard the horses taking on so, I came up the trail as quick and quiet as I could, and there you were risking your neck to save the horses. I said then and I'll say it again, only a brave lad would do a thing like that. You're a mite puny, but you're tough."

Flan felt fine as he thought this over, then his heart sank,

"But I lost the horses," he said to Mr. Green. "A real woodsman would have held them."

Mr. Green snorted. "Couldn't nobody hold horses as scared as they were. And don't worry none about them. We'll find 'em in the morning grazing close by. Trail horses get used to their folks and stick around 'em."

Flan felt better. Then another idea sprang at him.

"The Indians," he said. "Will they likely come back?"

"Shucks no," said Mr. Green as he began to mix their ash cakes for supper. "They're long gone from here."

He glanced up and grinned at the boy wrapped in his blanket beside the fire. "Thanks to you, Flan, we're sure enough going to get that powder safe to the French Salt Lick."

William O. Steele

Thinking About the Story

What did you learn about Flan and his opinion of himself in the very first part of the story? As the author tells about the journey, he hints of some other qualities in Flan. What are these qualities?

Flan saved the horses, but he was still concerned about something. What was it? What does this tell about Flan?

The title of the story tells you that Flan made good. Find and prepare to read aloud some of the things Mr. Green said to convince Flan of this.

How does the story prove that it isn't always size or strength that counts when it comes to showing real courage?

Saying It Another Way

Write the following sentences or parts of sentences in your own words:

> dark thunderheads piled up
> could read a trail
> pounding against the side of the mountain like
>   horses' hoofs
> I'm dry as the old well right now.
> What a wooden-head he'd been!

Imagining You Were There

The author chooses words that make you keenly aware of the violence of the storm, the terror of the horses, and Flan's own fear. What sounds would you have heard if you had been with Flan? What sights would you have seen? How would you have felt? Skim the story for several of the sights, sounds, and feelings which the author describes and arrange them in three lists headed: Sights, Sounds, Feelings.

Spurs for Antonia

ROMERO, the ranch foreman, was just putting the finishing touches on breakfast when the kitchen door opened.

"Am I on time, Romero?" whispered Antonia.

Romero turned from the stove to smile at the girl standing in the doorway.

"Manuela's still asleep," said the man, nodding in answer to her question.

Manuela was the ranch housekeeper, and Romero was her husband. They were dear to motherless Antonia, who had loved them well long before she had been sent away from the ranch to boarding school. Now she was back after three years away. She wanted above everything to stay here. Romero and Manuela and even Antonia's father thought of her now as a city girl. But Antonia loved best the ranch and the life on it. More than anything she wanted to prove to them all that here was where she belonged.

Though it was only four o'clock and still dark, she and Romero would soon be riding out of the corral to catch up with her father and the ranch outfit. The Boss, as the men called her father, had been in the hills with his cowboys for more than a week. They were rounding up the four thousand head of cattle that were scattered from the wide oak-shaded valleys of the flatlands to the rough, brushy wild country that lay far to the north and west, almost in sound of the sea.

Antonia sighed happily, thinking of the day ahead. Today she and Lucky were going to be part of a rodeo!

When breakfast was over and the kitchen left tidy, Antonia and Romero saddled their horses and rode out of the corral. With a quick slap of the reins on Lucky's flanks, Antonia hurried ahead to swing open the wide heavy gate.

The grass was high against their stirrups as they took the river trail. After the long late rains the feed had grown magically, tall and sweet and full of strength.

Humming a contented, wordless little song, Antonia let Lucky carry her along, his head tossing in time with the quick step of his hoofs and the jingle of bit and bridle. A smart cow pony knew what to expect on a fine spring morning like this. When the long line of bawling white-faced cattle wound off the hills, with the ranch outfit riding herd behind them, he would have his share in driving them to the holding corrals. There they would wait their turn for vaccination and branding.

Two hours later Romero touched his big gray horse with his spurs, and the horse shot ahead. Antonia slapped Lucky, and the two circled out into a wide loop that would bring them to the rear of the oncoming cattle's downhill swing.

With an excited shout, Antonia suddenly pulled up. "There they are!" she cried.

27

Sitting straight and eager in her saddle, she waved her hat wildly as the first of the herd topped the ridge and wound down the trail in an unending line.

Shading her eyes against the sun's glare, she spotted the Boss. She dug her heels into Lucky and rode forward to meet her father.

He smiled as she loped next to him. "Good work, cow-puncher. You must have started early to catch up with us. I've got a job ready for you. Want to ride along while I bring in those yearling calves up there in that gulch? They think they're hiding out on us, the little imps! Well, when we get them rounded up, we'll be through for the day. The men won't be sorry, and neither will I. It's been a tough week."

28

Suddenly he gave a shout and whirled his horse away from her and down the trail. Startled, Antonia looked beyond him to a cow pony that had taken it into his head to put on a show. He was bucking and lunging among the cattle, scattering the herd in all directions. His rider was sticking gamely, but the cow pony was beyond control. While Antonia stared, horrified, Romero rode past her galloping at top speed.

All along the line the cowboys closed in on the stampeding herd of cattle, shouting and yelling and prodding. Completely bewildered by the sudden confusion, her heart pounding hard, Antonia hung tightly to the reins and tried her best to quiet Lucky's excited prancing.

What was the best thing to do when you found yourself alone on a hillside, with a herd of excited cattle milling around down below you? One thing was sure—you had sense enough to keep out of the way.

She stared down the trail. Maybe Lucky wouldn't jump around so much if he had something interesting to do. What was it her father had said about a little bunch of calves up there on the side hill, in the brush? Why, of course! This was a chance to help.

Reining Lucky toward the brushy gulch that split a deep gash in the hillside, Antonia took the trail that climbed steeply through yellow mustard and tall grass. Far below she could hear the men shouting as they rode hard on the heels of the scattered herd, and turning in the saddle, she saw the dim shapes of cattle and horses moving through the brown dust of the river flat.

She let Lucky stop for a breathing spell and began to count the calves that were huddled ahead of her, under the shelter of a scrub oak thicket. Ten of them. They needn't think they could hide. Didn't they know that the Boss wanted them at the corrals? And that was where they were going.

She snatched off her hat and waved it wildly as she kicked her heels into her horse and sent him running along the trail. "Get along, Lucky boy! Yahoo-yipee! Yahoo!" Antonia shouted at the top of her lungs, trying to sound like the regular ranch hands.

The white-faced yearlings fixed astonished eyes on her for a moment, and then turned and broke into a run for the thick brush.

The grass and the mustard stalks had disappeared now. Rough sage and chaparral scratched Antonia's face and arms

as she ducked from thicket to thicket, trying to be in ten places at once. The calves ran from one brushy cover to another.

No sooner did Lucky have them covered and headed down hill than they broke away and scattered again in ten different directions. The little sorrel did his best, working with all the heart and intelligence of a seasoned cow horse. This way and that he turned, with Antonia half out of the saddle as he whirled to head off a calf.

Grabbing the horn of the saddle, she held on for dear life. Pulling leather was a big help—as long as no one was around to see you. If she could only hang on long enough, she and Lucky would have those calves just where they wanted them!

At last, one by one, the calves gave up their losing fight for freedom and dropped into line along the trail that led to the holding corrals and the river. Lucky kept close to their heels. The sorrel horse was not taking any chances, and at the first sign of a break, he was off again at a run, heading them back with a quick turn or a lightning jump that would throw Antonia out of the saddle onto his neck.

"It's all right with me, Lucky, whatever you want to do," she said, her hands aching from their grip on the reins, her knees rubbed sore as they clamped desperately. "You know lots more about roundups than I do."

Meanwhile, at the gate of the holding corral, the Boss turned to Romero with an anxious frown. "What do you suppose is keeping Antonia? I lost track of her in all the excitement, but I took for granted she was riding right behind us. Do you suppose she circled back and rode on home?"

Romero shook his head, his black eyes worried. "She was safe on the hillside, holding Lucky quiet, when I looked back the last time to make sure all was well. .Because the little sorrel is so gentle, because he has a head full of sense, I was not afraid to leave her alone. But now, if you have no more need of me, I'll ride back and look for her."

One of the cowboys perched on top of the fence rail broke into the conversation. "Guess you don't have to worry about your daughter any longer, Boss. Take a look at what's heading across the field!"

33

The Boss stared speechless at the dusty, hot, scratched, and shirt-torn rider astride her sweat-stained horse. Strung out ahead of her were ten yearling calves, and they were being headed straight for the holding corral.

Scrambling off the fence, the cowboy untied his horse and galloped off across the field to open the lower gate of the holding corral. Antonia and Lucky drove their calves through to the riverbank and watched them lurch over the side into the water.

Antonia took off her hat and fanned herself breathlessly. The noonday sun beat hotly on her tangled hair and on her dirty face. Her black eyelashes were gray with dust, and her pink cotton shirt was ripped on the right side in a long, brush-torn tear from shoulder to cuff. From her right eye to her chin a jagged red scratch made a bright path through the dust and sweat.

The Boss, spurring his horse, rode alongside her and put out his big hand, his eyes warm with approval and pride.

"Shake, cowpuncher! You handled those cattle like a top hand. The outfit says you're hired. You've moved right in. Matter-of-fact, I think you belong right here on the ranch with Manuela and Romero and me." He looked at her closely. "But tell me something. Whatever made you chase up the canyon after those yearlings, Antonia? What put the idea in your head?"

Antonia, with her grimy small hand in his, looked up at her father with surprised eyes.

"Well," she said simply, "you said you had a job for me. You said you wanted them in the corral, didn't you?"

Katherine Wigmore Eyre

Thinking About the Story

Antonia felt that she must work hard to prove something. What does she want to prove? Why?

Antonia was a girl who could think for herself and stay with a job until it was finished. Find sentences which show that this is true.

What did Antonia do that required courage? Do you think it is unusual for a girl to be able to do what she did? Tell about an incident from your experience or from your reading in which a girl acted with bravery.

There is a description at the end of the story which gives other clues to Antonia's character. Discuss what else this tells you about her.

The author says that Lucky worked "with all the heart and intelligence of a seasoned cow horse." What does this mean? How did Antonia show that she trusted Lucky?

Using Words to Describe

The author uses words such as *bucking, lunging,* and *prancing* to suggest the action of the roundup. List as many of these words as you can find in the story.

The author helps you to see the country in which the ranch was located by describing the thick brush and the rough sage. Find several descriptive phrases and be ready to read them to the group. Look for pictures of ranch life in magazines and choose a committee to arrange them in a bulletin-board display.

This story refers to many things that are part of life on a ranch. Tell what is meant by each of the following:

white-faced yearlings	the holding corral
little sorrel	vaccination and branding
horn of the saddle	ranch outfit

A Dog of the Alps

THE ALPS are as old as the world. Since time began, their lofty peaks have towered between the countries of Switzerland, France, and Italy. Many travelers have journeyed over these mountains in the years that have come and gone— armies on their way to war, pilgrims on their way to Rome, peddlers with their packs upon their backs. And many have perished there, overcome by the stinging winds, the snow, and the bitter cold.

At the top of one of the great passes there stands an ancient monastery known as the Hospice of Saint Bernard, in honor of a holy man whose self-sacrificing efforts placed it there almost a thousand years ago.

Bernard de Menthon, the holy man, had long dreamed of building a monastery there among the snows. A monastery would provide a safe stopping place for travelers forced to cross the Pass. Thus many lives could be saved.

And so the monastery was built. When it was completed,
Bernard had no difficulty in finding other monks who were
willing to share his life of hardship. They were brave men,
all of them, ready to sacrifice their own safety and comfort to
make life safer for others.

There have been many changes in the world since the
Hospice of Saint Bernard was first founded. But the Alps still
lift their snowy peaks toward the sky, and the bare stone
buildings of the Hospice still stand, grim and prison-like, more
than eight thousand feet above the valley floor.

The Pass is a well-kept road now, and the telephone and
radio can warn the monks of blizzards. Even so, the road is
impassable after the snows begin in November. From then
until May, the Hospice is sealed off from the rest of the world
and the monks go about on skis when they leave their
monastery walls.

During the summer season many tourists visit the Hospice, which for hundreds of years has been a famous spot. This is not surprising. Military leaders since the time of Hannibal and Caesar have led their armies past its site. And its monks, brave and learned, have served mankind well in many parts of the world. But the Hospice of Saint Bernard is most famous for its wonderful dogs. These huge, intelligent creatures have helped to save the lives of countless travelers lost in the snow.

One dog, Barry, most famous of them all, saved forty lives before he was killed by the forty-first person he rescued. This was a poor lost soldier who, almost overcome with cold and fear, thought the great furry creature pulling him out of a drift was some wild animal and stabbed him. The brave dog, his blood coloring the snow, dragged the man to the trail and then dragged himself to the Hospice to get help before he died.

Even today the monks at the monastery love to talk of this brave dog. Sometimes at evening, when they are gathered about the great log fire in the sitting room of the monastery, they will take down from a shelf an old diary of Brother Paul and read from its pages. Brother Paul trained Barry and was his master and friend as long as the dog lived.

Barry's training began when he was hardly more than a puppy. Each day he and his master went about over the neighboring mountainsides until Barry knew them almost as well as he knew his own kennel grounds. He soon learned the best paths to take in order to avoid the dangerous cliffs and canyons in the Pass.

Now it happened one night, when Barry had become grown, that Brother Paul suddenly felt as if someone outside were calling to him for help. He could not be sure it was anything more than the whistling of the wind that he had heard. But

the fancy was so clear that he sat up in bed and looked out of his small window.

It had been snowing hard for many hours, but the storm had passed, and he could see the great mountain peaks that rose, like shapeless giants, against the sky. All at once the moon broke through a rift in the clouds, and Brother Paul saw the black shape of a big dog standing alone in the kennel yard.

"Barry!" he exclaimed under his breath.

Just then the dog barked.

Brother Paul got out of bed, dressed quickly, and went out into the night. Barry was waiting for him at the kennel gate.

Quickly the monk strapped around Barry's neck a bundle of food and a small cask containing wine. "Good dog," he said, giving him a pat, and a moment later Barry was off down the mountain. Brother Paul was sure that Barry knew a traveler was lost along the trail, just as he had felt it in his bones.

The sky had cleared by this time. In the bright moonlight the monk could see Barry far ahead. Following the dog's lead, he made his way slowly through the thin crust of snow, for this was in the days before the monks had begun to use skis. The dog's hairy pads helped to support him on the snow crust, so he could travel faster than the man.

The traveler they sought was a peasant returning to his home. Two days ago he had reached the foot of the mountain, glad that soon he would be with his family. It was still early fall, and the workers had not yet finished gathering their grain.

"Surely," he thought, "there is time enough to make this journey before the bitter cold comes."

The first day of his journey all went well, and that night he stopped at one of the little shelters which the monks had built along the way. But it grew colder as he climbed, and toward noon of the second day heavy clouds began to roll across the sky. An icy wind whistled among the crags.

The peasant hurried on. "I can stand the cold," he thought, "if only the snow will hold off for a little while longer."

But the snow did not wait. Driven by the wind, it came whirling down the mountain, shutting the world from view. The poor peasant could not see the trail before him, but he struggled blindly on, hour after hour, until the cold had numbed him through and his strength was gone.

He was lost, as many another traveler had been lost before him. He could go no farther and wanted only to lie down and sleep. With one last call for help he sank upon the ground, where he lay very still while the snow slowly covered him.

He no longer felt the cold. He no longer heard the wind whistling across the Pass. He was sleeping, a sleep that must end in death unless help should come to him very soon.

40

But help did come, and it came in time. It came in the form of a big shaggy Saint Bernard dog who, in spite of the snow, had found the peasant's resting place and dug him out.

Little by little the half frozen man felt life returning. And when at last he opened his eyes, he found the big furry body of a dog stretched full upon him and a dog's soft warm tongue licking his face.

"It is one of the Saint Bernards from the Hospice," the peasant thought joyfully, and he reached for the food and wine that Barry carried round his neck.

Waiting only until the peasant had taken food and drink, Barry, barking loudly, started back to find his master. It was not long until he returned through the snow with Brother Paul.

The monk took off his coat and wrapped it about the peasant. Then, while Barry ran to the monastery to waken the monks, Brother Paul rubbed the traveler's numbed arms and legs. Finally he was able to get the man on his feet and safely back to the monastery.

A great log fire was blazing in the sitting room at the monastery, and a hot supper awaited the weary traveler. After he had finished his meal, he was wrapped warmly in blankets and put to bed.

The Hospice of Saint Bernard has seen its share of changes since the days when Brother Paul and Barry lived there. The years pass on, the monks grow old and die, and others come to take their places. But tales of Barry's brave deeds are still told round the monastery fire at night.

"There are no dogs in all the world like the dogs of Saint Bernard," the monks will end their story proudly. "They are a noble breed. But the noblest of them all was the great dog, Barry."

Alice Gall and Fleming Crew

Thinking About the Story

Why did Bernard de Menthon dream of building a monastery at the top of a great pass in the Alps? What words in the story describe him and the other monks who lived this life of hardship?

What changes have taken place since the Hospice was first built? What things have not changed?

Barry and his master, Brother Paul, seemed to have the same keen sense of knowing when help was needed. Find and read aloud a sentence from the story which proves this. What is meant by "the fancy was so clear that he sat up in bed?"

You will find two smaller stories within this story. Both of them are about rescues which Barry made. During which of these rescues did Barry show the greatest courage? Why do you think so? How were the stories of Barry's brave deeds passed on and remembered through the years?

Exploring Beyond the Story

A pass is a natural opening or path through a mountain range. There are two at the top of the Alps which are named for Saint Bernard. One is called Great and the other Little. Read in your encyclopedia about the Great Saint Bernard Pass where the famous Hospice stands. How high is it? What countries does it connect? Why has it been used for so many years by armies, pilgrims, and peddlers?

Try to find out all you can about the famous Saint Bernard dogs. What are some of the Saint Bernard's qualities that help it to find people lost in the snow? How is the dog suited to life in the Alps?

Look in other books for stories about Saint Bernard dogs. Plan to read them aloud to the group.

The Escape

NOBODY KNOWS why André Garnerin was imprisoned in the high tower at Budapest. Maybe he did not have enough money to pay his debts, or perhaps he had spoken against the Monarchy, for it was the time of the French Revolution. Whatever the reason was, he didn't want to stay there, and he kept trying to think of a way to get out.

It was not a particularly bad prison—just a tower built of blocks of stone, with the kites and the hawks wheeling over it all day. Three times a day an old warder with a heavy bunch of keys at his belt climbed up the narrow winding stair to bring him food. Otherwise he was alone all day, watching the sun as it went swinging across the sky, watching the stars at night.

He was not uncomfortable. At night the prison supplied a good bed in which to sleep. You might have expected a heap of straw spread on the floor, but Garnerin had a real bed, and oddly enough it seems to me, the bed was equipped with sheets and blankets.

44

However that may have been, he didn't like being there. He was the kind of man who liked doing things for the world of men to admire, not sitting alone in a tower all day. Sometimes he sat at the edge of the parapet, looking out across the red roofs of Budapest at the bending Danube River and the blue hills that folded away toward the horizon.

There was a green vine growing at the foot of the tower, but its growth was very slow. André had estimated that if it continued as it was growing now, he would be a man of ninety before it reached the place where he could climb down on it, and then he would be too old and stiff for the feat. And what good would it do him if he could then make his escape, for so little of his life would be left to him anyway? People who sit in prison towers often pass the time in trying to work out arithmetic problems like that.

45

Another way that André passed his time was in thinking about all the books he had ever read and all the stories he had ever heard so that he could see whether any of them would be useful to him now. It didn't take him very long to go over all the books, for he hadn't bothered to read very many. But when he began to think over all the stories he had heard, it took him a long, long time. For André Garnerin had been in many places, talked with many people, and sat for many hours at the tables of little inns—and that is the best place to listen to stories.

So one day as he sat beside the parapet of his strong prison tower, André remembered a story he had heard at an inn in England. A man interested in science had wanted to prove certain theories about air pressure or some such thing. So he had stepped off the top of a high stone wall, holding two strong open umbrellas in his hands. This gentleman, according to the story, had arrived safely on the earth.

It was obvious that André Garnerin had no umbrellas. And he did not think he could induce his guard to bring him any, for the weather was generally fair, and at any rate his prison had a very good roof. So André regretfully dismissed the idea of the umbrellas from his mind.

But it is a curious thing that when the seed of an idea is planted in the mind, although it is untended, it often grows like a weed. The idea of the umbrellas did not die; it grew.

At night when André Garnerin lay in his bed, he thought about the umbrellas, and all his dreams were filled with their rounded floating shapes. What were umbrellas made of? Cloth probably. What made them float so strong and steady in the air? Their shape probably, their rounded curving shape, like that of a child's soap bubble.

46

He was dreaming of umbrellas and soap bubbles one night when suddenly he found himself wide awake. He was so wide awake that he jumped out of bed and stood up on the cold stone floor. From his bed he tore the bed sheet which the prison had so curiously supplied. He went to the edge of the parapet, and all that night he sat holding his bed sheet, watching the gleaming stars, waiting for them to fade.

When the stars were dim, and the gray light of the morning had diluted the darkness, and the soft white mists were rising from the quiet earth as if to protect a man who had escaped, André Garnerin stood up beside the parapet. He took the big square bed sheet and put four hard knots in the corners. Then he fastened the four knots into one. Then he held it up, and a little puff of wind filled it until it was rounded like an umbrella. Then he closed his eyes, and murmuring a prayer, paused for a moment on the wall of the parapet, took a step forward, and jumped.

47

The bed sheet billowed and ruffled in the wind, then filled like a good strong sail set sideways. André Garnerin, clinging to the knots with both his hands, dropped down, swinging from side to side. The air rushed past him, but he kept his eyes tight shut. Down and down he dropped from the tower, from his prison, into freedom.

He landed with a crash in a thorny bush, and sat still waiting to see if anyone would come to get him. But no one came. The old warder was quite deaf.

André rubbed his ankles and his elbow, and found that he was not hurt. Then he tore a corner about six inches square from the bed sheet. Folding it carefully, he put it in his pocket for a souvenir and disappeared into the morning mist.

Now that he was free, what did André Garnerin do with his freedom? He made his way to France, which was a right and reasonable thing to do. There, wherever he heard that a crowd was to gather, for a horse race, or a fair, or for any other reason, he went aloft in a great balloon, and standing at the edge of the basket, with a wave to the crowd, he undid his parachute and jumped. He loved to do it. Sometimes he jumped a thousand feet, and sometimes he jumped two thousand feet.

Everybody began to talk about what he had done, which would have made the prison authorities rather nervous, only most of the prisons in Europe did not have towers, but dungeons. Men standing in the crowd to watch him shouted and cheered, and women fainted.

At first the swinging motion made him sick, so he couldn't fully enjoy the excitement of the crowds, but after a while he learned to cut a little hole in the top of the parachute so that the air passing through it stopped the swinging and made him fall straight as an arrow and graceful as an angel from heaven.

48

You might say it was not worth while for André Garnerin to get out of prison just to spend the rest of his life jumping out of a balloon. Yet every man to his taste, as they say. And I think the airmen who fly today, each one with his parachute neatly folded on his back, must be glad that he did it. That is, if they know anything about him at all.

Katherine B. Shippen

Thinking About the Story

 Perhaps you have heard the old saying, "Necessity is the mother of invention." How might this be true of the events in the story, "The Escape?"

Some sentences in the story give a clear picture of the life André Garnerin led while in the prison tower. Find three or four sentences that describe the tower, the furnishings, and the view. Read them to the group. Draw a picture to illustrate one of these sentences.

André Garnerin found things to do in order to pass away time while in prison. Did he spend his time profitably? How? What kind of a person do you think André must have been to jump from the parapet?

Exploring Word Meanings

The following are familiar words used by the author in unusual ways. What do they mean? How do they help to make the story interesting?

wheeling over it   seed of an idea
tore the bed sheet   bending Danube River

50

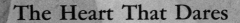

The Heart That Dares

Oh the stirring and rough and impetuous song—
The song of the heart that dares,
That keeps to its creed and gives no heed
To the faces that fortune wears.

That heart that laughs when the foe is met,
And thrives and fires at taunt and threat,
And finds no toiling and traveling long,
For the sake of the good it bears.

Author Unknown

51

The Wreck

THE DUSTIN FAMILY had been vacationing on Pine Island for one week when the storm broke. As the wind rose, Dave watched the tumbling gray water crash against the rocky shore. Dave lived in Colorado and had never been on an island before. Right now it seemed like a very small island surrounded by a large and powerful ocean.

Then the rain came, and it beat upon the cottage roof all day and all night. The storm was still going strong next morning when Dave woke up. But he had had enough of staying inside. He begged so hard to go out and see the surf that at last his mother said he might.

"Put on your raincoat and hat," she told him. "I know just how you feel. I always liked the storms when I came to Pine Island as a little girl."

Dave lost no time getting on his raincoat and hat and then he plunged out of the cottage into the teeth of the wind and rain. He fought his way to the shore, but before he got there, he could taste the salt in the air. The wind was tearing the tops off the breakers and whirling the spray past the shoreline.

He had been outside about an hour when he looked toward the harbor and saw men running along the shore.

"Something's happened," he thought.

He began to run toward the harbor, hoping that whatever had happened wouldn't be over before he got there.

Then he saw what the trouble was, and the words tumbled out of him and were lost in the wind.

"It's a boat! It's gone aground on the reef. It's a shipwreck!"

Dave was sure it was a freighter pinned to the reef. It was close enough to the island so he could see that it was tilted at a dangerous angle, the bow high, the stern low.

"It looks bad," he thought soberly, and the sea no longer seemed fun to watch. There was a threat in it as it attacked the helpless ship.

He ran to join the group of fishermen gathered on Bert Bibber's fish wharf. The men's sober faces and short, gruff remarks made Dave sure that the island men thought the ship was in grave danger of breaking up very soon.

"Doesn't seem right for us to stand on shore and watch those poor fellows on board her drown," said one man.

"It's too rough for a small boat to put out to her," said another. "I might risk it at that, but I have a family to think about."

"I'm not going to stand any more of this." Bert Bibber sounded angry. "I'm going to get the men off that ship."

"The sea will sweep into your boat. Your engine will never keep going with the water getting in it."

"I'm going in a dory," Bert shouted above the wind. "Going alone unless someone around here has the nerve to go with me. With two pairs of oars we can get close enough to her to take part of the crew off. At least we can try."

"Take me," Dave wanted to say, longing to go with Bert, but he knew that Bert would need stronger arms than his.

"I'm not afraid to get my feet wet," said one of the fishermen. "I'm with you, Bert. How about taking along a barrel of oil? Throwing oil on the water close to the ship might calm the sea a mite."

"There's a barrel with a spigot in it over in my shed," said Bert. "Put the oil in that one. It'll be easier to handle it that way."

Two men ran to Bert's shed for the barrel. Somebody went for a rope. Bert went for a second pair of oars. One man

54

shouted that he had an inner tube that might serve for a life preserver. Everybody but Dave suddenly found something to do to help. He was left alone on the wharf while the others rushed around. He looked out and saw small moving figures at the bow of the wrecked freighter. They would be drowned unless somebody got to them soon. Dave longed to do something for them. He just *had* to!

Almost without knowing what he was doing, Dave went down the ladder on the side of the wharf where Bert's dory had been pulled up. He was just going to look at the dory close to, but when he saw a tarpaulin in the dory's bow, something made him climb in and hide under it. He was shivering with excitement. He was going along with the two men to help rescue the freighter's crew. He wasn't afraid to go. Like Bert, he couldn't stand on shore and watch the men drown. He did not reason out why he hid instead of asking Bert to take him. He was too excited to know why he was doing anything.

Now he heard the men coming back. Dave felt the dory lurch as the oil barrel was lifted aboard.

"This dory's used to rough water," said Bert, as he and the other man took their places in the boat. Not Bert but the other man was in the bow seat, so near that Dave could have reached out and touched him. Then the oarlocks creaked as the men began to row.

The water in the harbor was rough, but it was nothing to what the dory met outside. Mountains of water were under the small boat, sliding avalanches of sea on all sides. Dave peeked out, and the nearness and the wildness of the sea frightened him as nothing ever had frightened him before in all his life. This ocean was awful.

He wished with all his heart that he had stayed ashore. What good would it do the men on the sinking ship for him to drown? He was afraid now all right—afraid that any minute the dory would be swamped and that he and Bert and the other man would be swallowed by the sea. Dave seemed to sense its readiness to gulp them down as the dory sank sickeningly deep in the trough of a wave, then rose up, up.

56

"I want to go home," Dave sobbed, pulling away the tarpaulin. "I don't want to be drowned. I want to go home."

"What's a baby doing here with us!" cried the man at the bow. "I didn't agree to take babies along. What business you got to be here, anyway?" Though his voice was almost lost in the storm, Dave heard the hard words clearly enough.

However, that was nothing compared to what Bert Bibber said when he caught sight of Dave. The sea was noisy, the wind was howling, yet Bert's voice could have been heard above a cyclone. "Just plain fool-in-the-head and hardly worth drowning," roared Bert. "One more word out of you and I'll throw you overboard myself."

Dave shrank into himself and wished he could shrink further. The sudden rush of Bert's anger almost made him forget his fear of the sea.

He was so drenched and miserable by now that he hardly noticed when the waves flung great slops of water over the side.

"Take that . . . and that," the slap of the waves seemed to say to a boat pitifully weak and small. Yet the men at the oars were fighting the sea hard. They were doing more than keeping the dory from capsizing. They were slowly making their way toward the wrecked freighter. Now they were close enough so that Dave could see the faces of the men standing at the ship's bow. They all had the same dazed expression. That must be how it looked to be afraid of being drowned.

"Now that you're here," Bert shouted at Dave, "you've got to help. You've got to get to the stern and turn on the spigot in that oil barrel. It takes two of us at the oars. Come on, now, crawl along the bottom and get at it."

"But I can't."

"You've got to. Get!"

The lash of Bert's voice sent Dave crawling along the heaving bottom of the boat. Water washed about him, but he hardly noticed that. He was numb with fear, but his body did what Bert commanded it to do.

Then, just before Dave reached the stern of the dory, something in him changed. He suddenly stopped being so scared. He just thought quite calmly how he could best hang on with one hand while he turned on the spigot with the other.

With his left hand he clung to the dory while with the right he worked at the spigot. It stuck.

"Hurry!" barked Bert.

It would take both hands. He might go overboard, but he had to turn that spigot. Dave was just willing his left hand to join the right when the spigot turned and the oil began to pour over the side.

58

One barrel of oil had very little effect on the sea, yet it may have given a minute or two when the rough water between dory and freighter smoothed over ever so slightly. The man at the bow got a rope to the freighter just as another dory arrived with more oil to pour on the sea. Two more dories were coming. The island fishermen had decided to help with the rescue.

Bert took three men off the freighter. Another dory was moving up, so he thought it best not to overload his boat.

"Nasty day," said one of the men rescued, just as if a remark about the weather were the proper thing to say. Another man said, "much obliged," and still another said that he would be glad to get on a pair of dry socks. Not a man said a word about the wrecked ship, but Dave saw the sailor who had wanted dry socks keep gazing back at it with a sad, lost look in his eyes. He looked as if he felt the way Dave had felt when his dog had been run over by a car.

Dave was still shaking with
excitement when Bert's dory reached
the harbor. There the sound of the
waves slapping under the motorboats
seemed like hands clapping in
applause. A few minutes later Dave
realized the blessing of having dry
land under his feet. It felt
comfortingly solid.

Once ashore, Dave wanted to hang
around, but Bert grabbed him and
told him to get along home as fast as
he could leg it. "Next time wait till
you're asked before you ship along
with me," he said harshly. "What
do you think your father would have
said to me if you'd been drowned?"

Dave thought that if he had been drowned, Bert probably would have been too. He thought that Bert might at least have thanked him for turning on the spigot in the oil barrel. But he could tell that his company wasn't wanted around there. He walked off along the shore, climbing over the wet ledges.

When he got home, his mother asked, "Did you see the wreck? Were the men saved?"

"They were saved all right," said Dave. He didn't want to talk about the shipwreck. He could still remember every one of Bert's angry words.

After a while Mr. Dustin came in. He had been down to the harbor in time to see the last of the freighter's crew brought in. The islanders had done a brave thing, he said, going out in a rough sea and risking their lives. He looked hard at Dave, but Dave was looking at the floor, dreading to have his father scold him for going along with Bert.

Later, when Dave and his father were alone, Mr. Dustin said, "I hear you invited yourself to join the rescue party."

Dave was silent.

Mr. Dustin did not sound angry, but his blue eyes were grave. "There's a very thin line between recklessness and bravery," he said. "Sometimes I think there's even an element of bravery in recklessness. I'm glad you're no coward, Dave, but that was a pretty silly thing to do. It turned out all right, but it wasn't fair to make Bert have the responsibility of looking after you."

"But he didn't. He made me—" Dave was stammering.

"I know what you did. I got it out of Bert. You were of some use. But he was in charge, and it wasn't right for you to go along without his consent."

"But he wouldn't have let me go if he'd seen me."

"Then you had no right to go."

"But I had to. I wanted—"

"It was a man's job, not a boy's. The space you took up in the dory might have cost some man his life. Don't ever again go anywhere when you have to hide in order to be taken along. It's not a grown-up way to act. Now I'm not going to tell your mother about this. If I did, she might begin worrying if you're out of her sight. Time enough to tell her if somebody else talks about it. All right?"

It was all right with Dave if nobody talked about it again.

There was a silence between them, and then Dave said, "Bert's mad at me."

"He's over being mad now. He sent word by me that if you want to, you may go out to haul his lobster pots with him tomorrow morning. He says the weather's going to clear. He starts at six."

Dave had longed to go out with Bert for lobsters.

"I wake up early," he said.

All at once Dave realized that it was not even drizzling now. He looked out at the swiftly moving clouds.

"Yes," said his father. "I think the storm's over."

Hazel Wilson

Thinking About the Story

Dave had a vacation experience that he would long remember. How do you think this experience will help him the next time he visits the island? Compare the place where Dave spent his vacation with the place in which he lived.

Dave enjoyed watching the storm on the ocean until he saw that there was a threat in it. What was the threat?

Dave felt that he just *had* to help the men on the wrecked freighter, but he acted without thinking. How could this have led to real trouble for himself and others? Why did some of the men not wish to help with the rescue at first? What made them change their minds?

Do you think the only reason for Mr. Bibber's anger was the inconvenience of having a small boy aboard? What other concern might have been hidden behind his anger?

Dave's father said, "There's a very thin line between recklessness and bravery . . . Sometimes I think there's even an element of bravery in recklessness." What do you think he meant? Discuss a situation in which you, or someone you know, may have done something partly out of recklessness, and partly out of bravery.

Finding Words That Describe

In the opening paragraphs the author gives a feeling of the mood and the atmosphere of the story by describing the taste of salt in the air and the wind tearing the tops off the breakers. Find other vivid descriptions and read them to the group.

Words can help to create a feeling of the power and the sound of the stormy sea. Use some of the author's words in a paragraph or a poem describing a storm at sea.

The Attack

ABIGAIL stopped at the window on her way to the pantry
and watched the colt come tearing across the meadow,
scattering flying clouds of turf behind him. It was a fine
spring day with a southwest wind and hurrying clouds and a
smell of the budding woods beyond the clearings. Abigail
smiled at the little horse's frolicsomeness. But a moment later
she frowned. Jenny, the old mare, had appeared at a more
ponderous gallop and was wheeling and stamping by the gate.

"Something has disturbed the horses, sir," Abigail said, turning to her father. "Do come and see."

Mr. King moved from the fire to the window and chuckled
as he watched Jenny and her colt. He pinched his daughter's
cheek.

"It's the fine gaiety of spring, my child," he said. "Something
has disturbed the robins, too. Hear how they are singing in
your mother's lilac bush."

64

Mrs. King, who had been clearing away the bowls and pewter from the table, hesitated and then asked her husband a question.

"You don't think it could be savages, Enoch?"

"The crows have all flown up," said Abigail quickly from her place by the window.

Her father gave a grunt of impatience.

"You women dream of savages," he said. "If you hear a mouse in the wall, it's a savage; if a bullfrog croaks, it's a war cry to you. There's no trouble with the tribes, and the Prebles' garrison house is just a stone's throw from our back door. You're as safe as if you were living in Pemaquid Fort."

Mrs. King went softly out with the dishes, and Abigail said nothing more. Her father was one of those large good-natured men who laugh a great deal, but who are quickly made angry by any argument.

Abigail slipped out to the woodpile where her brother was splitting firewood.

"John," she said, "something's wrong. The horses are wild, and the crows are flying up. Father says it's just their high spirits, but the sheep are huddling, too. That's not high spirits."

John gave a hasty look, spit on his hands, and went on splitting wood.

"You and Mother are a couple of scare-cats," he said. "Sheep are always huddling about something or other. You don't catch Aunt Phipps worrying over every little thing.

John was only fourteen, a year younger than Abigail, but lately he had taken to aping his father's hearty ways. Aunt

Jane Phipps, Mr. King's widowed sister who lived with them, was the same. She had three little children, Eunice and Samson and Kate, all round-headed and round-eyed and casual. Even down to small dimpling Kate, they seemed to go deaf if anyone tried to tell them that they were doing a thing the wrong way.

"It may have been a fox," thought Abigail. "There is no reasonable reason for my feeling so sure that the savages are nearby watching us."

But all day long she went about her work, more silent than usual. She seemed to be listening for something. Her father and Aunt Phipps, young John and the children were busy and boisterous all day, but her mother looked tired and anxious.

The only other member of the household to seem disturbed was Mittens, the cat, a big gray tom who followed the family about like a dog and would even walk a mile or two with them. This day he mewed about people's feet and seemed unable to keep still, moving from one favorite spot to another.

That night Abigail, in her little room at the head of the stairs, slept well, tired out with anxiety. Once she woke to feel Mittens jump on her bed, a thing he had rarely done before, but she was soon asleep again. In the morning, however, she was disturbed by finding several footprints in the soft earth under the windows. Aunt Phipps, her arms full of wet clothes she was bringing out to spread on the grass, came up to her as she stood examining the marks.

"Bless us, child," she exclaimed. "You're still fretting over your savages. No, they don't look like moccasin tracks to me. But I did see young John there yesterday morning, cleaning up last year's rubbish. You take my advice, Abigail, and think of something else."

That morning her father announced that he meant to make use of the good weather. He would take some grain to the town to be ground and a couple of lambs for sale. John was to go with him, and they would not be back until late that night.

"But, Enoch," began Mrs. King anxiously.

"But nothing, Mary!" cried her husband. "Pluck up heart, my love! Look at Sister Phipps here. She's not afraid. There's no danger, or I shouldn't be leaving you, and that you well know. But if any more of Abigail's crows fly from one field to another, you have only to run over to the Prebles' and you'll be perfectly safe at the garrison house."

"There's only the old man and Mr. Preble," ventured Mrs. King, but she stopped at her husband's angry look.

"You two will drive me mad with your whining," he exclaimed, shrugging his shoulders impatiently. "Come, wife, don't play the coward. Give me a cheerful fare-ye-well and no more nonsense."

68

An hour after Mr. King and John had ridden away, the Indians came. They had evidently been watching from the woods and waited only until the two were well out of hearing of gunshot. There were five of them, their faces streaked and splashed with vermilion and black, set off with bright blue, naked except for their breechclouts, but each with a gun over his arm. They separated and approached the house from different sides.

Aunt Phipps had time to snatch Eunice from the doorstep and bolt the door. Abigail ran to fasten the shed door and came back to find that her aunt had got the loaded gun down from the mantel.

"I'll fill those savages with lead," she was saying. "I never yet was afraid of any man, white or red!"

Abigail's mother snatched at the barrel.

"You must do nothing of the sort, Sister Phipps!" she said quickly and commandingly. "You could never hurt more than one, and they would kill all your children. They can knock a hole in this flimsy house in five minutes and fire through it.

69

I'm going to let the Indians in and feed them. It's our only chance."

"You've gone mad with fear!" cried Aunt Phipps, shouldering the lighter woman aside once more.

"Abigail!" said her mother, and Abigail snatched the gun unexpectedly from her aunt and stood with it behind her.

"Quick, Sister Phipps!" said her sister-in-law. "Take the children and get into the kitchen closet. When I let the Indians in, the way to the garrison house will be clear. While I am feeding them, Abigail and you are to get the children over the stockade and into the Prebles'."

"But they'll kill you for certain, Sister King!" cried Aunt Phipps, wringing her hands.

"If they do, you and the children will still have a chance," said Mrs. King.

There was a battering at the door.

"I'll stay here with you, Mother," said Abigail. "When the Indians are busy eating, you must be the one to help Aunt Phipps get away with the children. Then I'll join you."

Her mother gave her a quick look, sighed, and nodded. Aunt Phipps and her brood were gone.

"Bring the rum and mugs, child," she said, and smoothing out her skirts, walked over to the door and opened it with a strained smile. Two savages rushed in, brandishing their tomahawks. At their yell, the others ran from behind the house and poured in also.

"Rum," said Mrs. King, smiling still and pointing to the table, where Abigail, her heart pounding in her throat, had brought out rum and mugs. As she turned her back, she saw one of the savages snatch at the string of gold beads about her mother's neck. The chain that held them broke and the beads fell in a shower over the floor. At the same moment she heard the sharp slap of her mother's hand on the Indian's arm, but Abigail walked steadily over to the cupboard and came back with a plate of johnnycake. When she turned, she saw that the savages were laughing. They greedily grabbed the bread from the plate and began eating it in large mouthfuls. They were very hungry.

Her mother went into the next room and came back with a half-eaten leg of cold lamb which she set before the Indians. As she went out again, her eyes met Abigail's for an instant to tell her that she was going to try to make her escape. She had been gone only a minute when one of the Indians made as if to follow her.

Abigail had an impulse to throw herself in front of the door. Instead, she climbed onto a chair and began to search the upper shelves of the cupboard beside the mantelpiece, smacking her lips. The Indian halted to watch her. She must take as much time as she could, but she must not lose his interest. She rummaged about noisily, hoping to cover the sound of creaking floor boards or the gentle opening of a door. Just as she felt the Indian about to move again toward the kitchen, she brought down the heavy jug of molasses which she knew was kept there away from the children. Then she placed more johnnycake on five wooden plates and, watched by five pairs of unwinking eyes, poured the molasses over each piece. She was all alone in the house with the Indians, but by this time she was so excited that she had passed into a sort of calm in the middle of the storm.

"Eat!" she said, smiling as her mother had smiled, and gave each a plate into which they dipped their hands, greedily, dripping and sticky.

They had never tasted the stuff before and were lost in the pleasure of the moment. The room reeked with the odor of rum and bear's grease. The girl brought them more johnnycake and poured more molasses for them.

Surely even heavy Aunt Phipps must be over the stockade fence now. The black eyes glittered at her from the painted masks of the savages' faces. Abigail could not tell whether they suspected her or not. She walked over to the fireplace and mended the fire. Three minutes more. At any moment they would be wondering what had delayed her mother, and then she would be lost. She took a platter from the dresser as if to bring still more food and walked into the next room.

A glance showed her that the closet door was open, and the closet empty, though the outside door had been closed again, probably to avoid a telltale draught. It would be her mother who had thought of that. She put down the platter, opened the door softly, and as she closed it felt something at her feet. It was Mittens, looking terrified. She caught up the

72

cat. He would not be left behind if she could help it. Then gathering her skirts with her left hand to keep them from catching in the spring brambles, she ran toward the stockade fence a hundred yards away.

She saw her mother's white face in an upper window of the garrison house; then she heard a shout behind her, caught her foot in a bramble, and pitched headlong, flinging Mittens forward as she fell. She was up in a moment, stumbling over her skirts. She saw the Indians running toward her. One was standing leveling his gun. She ran forward, ducked suddenly to pick up Mittens, heard a shot ring over her where her head had been, and ran on. She saw Mr. Preble's face appear over the stockade wall.

"Quick, Abigail!" he shouted, reaching down for her. She threw the clawing cat over the six-foot stockade, held up her wrists, and in a moment felt herself being dragged painfully up the rough side of the wall and hauled to safety.

Once on the ground, Mr. Preble caught her about the waist and ran toward the garrison house. Another shot rang out behind them, answered by a shot from one of the upstairs windows. Then the door flew open, women's hands drew them into the semidarkness of the room, and the door was bolted again.

"Oh, my love!" cried Mrs. King, seizing Abigail in her arms. "I feared you would never come out of that house alive."

"If it wasn't for you two, we'd all be dead," said Aunt Phipps, red-faced and serious. "I owe you an apology, Sister King, for calling you a coward."

"But I am a coward," said Mrs. King, trembling and smiling. "I must get back to making my bullets. We may need all that I can make."

Abigail followed Mr. Preble up to the second story. Downstairs the shutters had all been closed, but here the light shone sweetly in upon the wide boards of the floor and the quilted covers of the feather beds.

Let them burn her father's house, if they would. It was only flesh and blood that counted. She looked out the window, tired, but curiously peaceful.

Crows were wheeling black against the sky. Something had disturbed them. Yes, there were figures moving out along the lane toward the north. Two of them were carrying a wounded Indian on a litter made from the back of the settle; the other two were laden with the covers of feather beds filled with loot.

"Mr. Preble!" she called. "The Indians are going!"

"I've been watching them," he said regretfully. "Too far off to get a shot. Father, you stay here and fire off your gun if you see them turn. Abigail and I will see if they've set the house on fire."

They found the King place in great confusion. Everything was pulled about and feathers were flying like snow. The fire had been hauled out onto the floor, but was only charring the stout boards; a couple of buckets of water from the well turned it to black soot and wet cinders. The Indians had taken all the food they could lay hands on, a few knives and ornaments, and the gun which Abigail had snatched from Aunt Phipps.

"You have been fortunate," said Mr. Preble. "If only—"

Abigail understood. The Indians had been in hiding for at least a day before they made the attack; they had watched the family at supper through the windows; they had come, finally, when the women were defenseless. Now, although they had seemed to go north, they might still be lying in wait somewhere for the return of Mr. King and John.

Abigail opened the door and looked out. The light was golden with late afternoon, and two butterflies passed in zigzag flight. Beyond the fields and meadows the crows were beginning to roost, lighting in the tops of the beeches and uttering their usual cries. Then a shape moved along the side of the house, and Mittens sat down solidly on the doorstep and began to smooth his ruffled coat with a white paw.

"No," said Abigail, laughing a little hysterically. "I'm sure Father and John are safe and the savages altogether gone. Mittens is washing his whiskers."

Elizabeth Coatsworth

76

Thinking About the Story

 Abigail had a feeling that something was wrong. What were some of the signs that made her think so? Did anyone else in the family share her feelings and worries? Who?

Discuss what Aunt Phipps and Abigail's mother each did when the Indians came. Which one do you think acted more wisely and showed the greater courage? Why?

Abigail showed courage when she was faced with danger. How did her quick thinking and bravery help to save the family? Tell how Mittens played an important part in the story.

Because the family faced great danger, the story is full of suspense. What part held the most suspense for you?

Using Words to Describe

Vivid descriptions and phrases make the story more enjoyable. Below are descriptions of some of the story characters. Tell to whom each refers.

he had taken to aping his father's hearty ways

they . . . were lost in the pleasure of the moment

she had passed into a sort of calm in the middle of the storm

all round-headed and round-eyed and casual

Finding Word Pictures

This story begins with a vivid word picture. Find another word picture at the end of the story. How do these word pictures help to create a feeling for the setting of the story? Be prepared to read both of them to the group.

Find another word picture in the story. Draw an illustration of it.

A Song of Greatness

When I hear the old men
Telling of heroes,
Telling of great deeds
Of ancient days,
When I hear them telling,
Then I think within me
I too am one of these.

When I hear the people
Praising great ones,
Then I know that I too
Shall be esteemed,
I too when my time comes
Shall do mightily.

A Chippewa Indian Song
Transcribed by Mary Austin

Animals All

Hunting the Haunt Fox

S NOW HAD FALLEN during the night. A light dusting of it
lay upon the farmyard, and the black clouds overhead
promised more to come. Jack Crowley broke shell ice on the
watering trough so that the horses could drink.

It had been a good season in the valley, and a busy one.
The barns were filled to bursting with hay and grain, and cellars
groaned with shelf after shelf of canned goods. Now at last
the hot, hard summer was over, and there would be more
leisure.

Jack's eyes glowed with anticipation as he glanced at the
hills, for to him leisure meant hunting foxes with Thunder,
his great hound.

The horses drank their fill and turned back toward the barn.
Jack's father, Jeff Crowley, who had been cleaning stalls, leaned
on his shovel as one of the big horses crowded past him.

80

"Aiming to get out in the hills with Thunder?" he asked as his son entered the barn.

Jack grinned. "I'd like to."

"Go ahead," said Jeff. "There's hardly enough work around here today to keep one man busy."

He stood with his son in the barn door. Together they looked at the snow-powdered hills.

"All right," said Jack. "I'll go see if Thunder and I can find a . . . Look!"

A red fox had leaped out of the corn shock where it had been quietly waiting. It sprang on one of the plump farm pigeons feeding in the barnyard, then streaked toward the near-by hills.

"Look at that fellow go!" said Jeff, half in admiration. "He must have been waiting in that corn shock since before daylight."

The two men crossed the field at a dogtrot. Side by side they reached the place where the fox had hidden. A few blue feathers lay among the evenly spaced tracks of a running fox. Though only a few tracks remained, there could be no doubt about who had made them.

"The Haunt Fox again!" Jeff said.

The Haunt Fox had earned his name by his ghostly habits. Every farmer for miles around had vowed to "get" him. But so far no one had. He boldly entered their barnyards and stole their fowl almost from under their very eyes. Then when the hunt was on, he eluded them as easily as if he possessed some magic to make him invisible. The best hounds in the valley had been loosed upon his trail, but no hound had been fast enough or smart enough to lead the hunters to where the Haunt Fox stood at bay.

Now Jack's blood raced. He was remembering the thrilling sound of a hound tonguing on a fox's trail, and the times he had drawn his shotgun on a fox running ahead of Thunder. There had been all kinds, from young ones to wise old dog foxes. But never the Haunt Fox. And now here he was in the Crowley barnyard. Or at least he had been here only minutes ago!

Jack raced toward the house. Quickly he filled one pocket of his wool hunting jacket with shells, and took up his shotgun. Then he went outside to the back of the house where Thunder was chained.

Seeing the gun, the great hound leaped with excitement. His excited baying echoed through the distant hills. When Jack reached down to unsnap his chain, Thunder danced a crazy circle around him.

In an instant he scented the fox track and swung to it. His head went down, his tail stiffened. For a moment he snuffled noisily about. Then a deep bay rolled from his chest, and he raced away on the track.

Meanwhile the Haunt Fox, safe in the brush, had stopped to eat the pigeon. Then at a slow trot he headed deeper into the hills. He had scarcely started when Thunder's baying broke the morning silence. The Haunt Fox stopped and looked back, his eyes sparkling. He knew from the voice that the hound was Thunder, and he had a great respect for Thunder, but he did not feel any fear. Though he knew that it would be hard to shake this hound from his tracks, he was certain of his ability to do it. The hound was not the real danger he must face. The hunter who would be with the hound was deadly. At all costs the fox must avoid him.

In a sudden burst of speed he left Thunder behind, then settled down to an easier pace. He circled through the brush, and from a high point looked down on the Crowley farm. There was nothing to be seen except the buildings, and the fox ran on.

For an hour he made no special effort to leave any breaks in his trail. Then he waded a creek, knowing as he did so that such a trick would not delay Thunder very long.

He left the water and struck a trail through a laurel thicket. Twisting and turning a dozen times, he raced out of the laurel as Thunder entered it. Then he ran to a little hillock and waited for Thunder to untangle the snarled trail he had left.

A mediocre hound would have been confused, but Thunder was not mediocre. He needed only minutes to discover what the fox had done and to cut across the thicket and pick up the trail beyond. Seeing the hound emerge from the laurel,

the Haunt Fox got up to run again. This time he laid his course through a grove of small hardwoods, traveling at a fast lope. Suddenly he called on every ounce of speed he had and flashed at right angles to the path he had intended to take.

Jack Crowley was standing in the hardwoods when the fox came into them, and saw the fox as the fox saw him. Jack did not shoot because the fox was out of range. At a fast walk Jack started toward the next place where he expected the Haunt Fox to appear.

The fox ran straightaway, putting as much distance as possible between himself and the hunter. Faint and far away, he could hear Thunder's steady baying. Though the hound was not nearly so fast as the fox, he had great endurance. The fox waded another creek and made his way toward a gully full of scattered boulders.

Before venturing among the boulders, where few trees and no brush grew, he checked the area carefully from all sides. At last, certain that no hunter waited hidden there, he made a long spring to the top of one, leaped from that to another, and so to a third. Jumping from boulder to boulder, he reached the edge of the woods and vanished among the trees.

For the first time Thunder slowed. He knew most of a fox's tricks, but this was a new one. He needed a while to figure it out.

Meantime the fox ran through a herd of deer grazing on a sheltered hillside so that their scent mingled with his own. Then running on up the hillside, he found a thicket and sat down with his tail curled around his rear paws.

86

Faintly in the distance he heard Thunder baying and knew from the sound that he had not yet shaken the hound from his trail. At a fast run the fox set off across the hilltop.

Morning waned into afternoon, early evening shadows gathered, and still Thunder came. Tiring and hungry, the Haunt Fox needed time to rest and to hunt. But he dared not stop as long as Thunder pushed him so hard.

A certain memory began forcing his weary steps into a wide circle which took him back into the hills and toward a remembered ledge of rock where, once during the summer, he had left another farmer's hound confused. The ledge was a tricky place, and he was still sure that no hound could get down it. Arrived there, he leaped to the first paw hold, down to the second, and to the third. He sprang from the ledge as he had done that other time—and landed squarely in a trap!

Twenty minutes later Thunder appeared on top of the ledge. Finding no way to get down, he wakened the wilderness with deep-toned baying.

All day long Jack had followed the Haunt Fox's trail, guided by the baying of his hound. He had caught glimpses of his quarry now and then and once, in among the hardwoods, he had almost had a shot at him. He felt only a warm excitement that spoke of good fortune. The Haunt Fox was proving worthy of his name. He was as elusive as a ghost.

Now he climbed another hill from which he could get a good view. Night was coming, and more snow would come with it, but Jack did not care.

As he stood on the high ridge, a sound came to him so faint and far off that he couldn't be sure whether it was Thunder tonguing or merely some trick of the wind. Then it came again, strong this time, and he knew it was Thunder's voice. It was coming steadily from one place. Listening, Jack tried to figure out what was happening. Slowly his heart sank. The Haunt Fox, after all, was not the magnificent creature he had thought. It was not a superior fox at all. It had gone to earth, sought safety in a burrow, like any frightened cub!

Wearily he made his way toward the sound of Thunder's baying. While he was still a hundred yards away, he saw the hound looking down from the top of a rock ledge and still baying. Jack walked up beside the dog and looked down too.

The fox was lying perfectly still, pressed close to the earth he loved and not moving at all. Jack peered down through the lengthening shadows and saw the trap on the fox's foot. For a long moment he just stood there, his hand on Thunder's neck. Then he snapped the chain on Thunder's collar and led him around the ledge. Tying the hound to a small tree, he walked slowly up to the Haunt Fox.

When the man was three feet from him, the Haunt Fox leaped to the end of the trap chain, and his sharp fangs left a clean rip in Jack's heavy pants. Then Jack's foot was on him. With his boot he pressed the fox to earth. As gently as possible he held him there, while his hands slipped around the Haunt Fox's neck. With his knee he pressed down the trap's springs, and as soon as the jaws loosened, he lifted the fox out. Almost in the same motion he cast the animal away from him.

For a second they faced each other, the courageous hunted and the sporting hunter. Then the Haunt Fox slipped like a shadow into the gathering gloom and was gone.

Jim Kjelgaard

Thinking About the Story

 The Haunt Fox had an unusual name. Why was he given this name? Why had the farmers not been able to "get" him?

How long a time did Jack and Thunder trail the Haunt Fox? How did the Haunt Fox try to throw Thunder off his trail? The story says that "A mediocre hound would have been confused, but Thunder was not mediocre." Be ready to explain the word *mediocre* and to read sentences from the story to prove Thunder was not mediocre.

What happened when the Haunt Fox made a last attempt to trick Thunder?

This story has a surprise ending. Why do you think Jack let the Haunt Fox out of the trap? The story describes the Haunt Fox and Jack as "the courageous hunted and the sporting hunter." Do you agree with these descriptions? Why or why not?

Understanding the Story Setting

At what time of the year does this story take place? The author gives a feeling for the season by the way he describes the sky, the barnyard, the work of the past summer, and other things. Find and be ready to read aloud several of the descriptive sentences.

In what sections of the United States might this story have taken place? Find evidence in the story to support your opinion. You will need to think about the seasonal changes, wildlife, trees and other plants, the land, and the activities of the people. Be ready to discuss your clues with the group.

Compare the setting for this story with the region where you live. Make a list of the likenesses and differences.

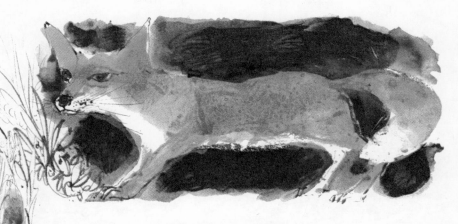

Night of Wind

How lost is the little fox at the borders of night,
Poised in the forest of fern, in the trample of wind!
Caught by the blowing cold of the mountain darkness,
He shivers and runs under tall trees, whimpering,
Brushing the tangles of dew. Pausing and running,
He searches the warm and shadowy hollow, the deep
Home on the mountain's side where the nuzzling, soft
Bodies of little foxes may hide and sleep.

Frances Frost

March of Death

THIS IS THE STORY of a curious migration. It concerns a small rodent that lives on the Scandinavian peninsula. These rodents are called lemmings. Once every three or four years the lemmings begin a march of death. Their migration from the mountain uplands above the timberline to the sea ends in the death of every traveler.

Lemmings are close cousins of rats and mice, and are the most common rodent in arctic and subarctic regions. They live in their own crowded cities. Each lemming is protected from the bitter cold of the long northern winter by a thick coat of yellowish-brown fur. Each lemming has its own grass-lined burrow which is attached to a storeroom stocked with moss, roots, and seeds. This arrangement allows a hungry lemming to have breakfast in bed.

If lemmings were not such friendly creatures, they would have a serious traffic problem. A maze of tunnels connects every burrow to others, while thousands of corridors cross and recross the cities in every direction. Some are deep in the ground. Others run along the surface. All day long these roadways are crowded with lemmings seeking food or returning to their burrows to sleep. However, there is no confusion as in our cities during rush hour. Lemmings greet one another by touching noses. Then they make room to pass.

Street construction never stops in these underground cities. Always hungry, lemmings are forever adding to their network of tunnels as they search for moss and lichens. The tunnels that are dug in the winter protect their users because of the snow cover. But in the spring, when the rodents are anxious to gorge themselves with green shoots, they merely make pathways through the grass. Hawks, owls, and foxes soon learn where these carelessly laid-out roads are and prey upon the traffic. Although many of the city's inhabitants are destroyed by talons and teeth, the population grows larger every day.

This is because the females have three to five litters each year. Moreover, their children become parents when very young. And so, more burrows and tunnels have to be dug, and the city fans out in all directions. If food is plentiful, the litters are larger than usual and the number of lemmings increases enormously. Because of this, their natural enemies have a greater food supply and they too have larger families. Yet the population of the city continues to grow. Before long it becomes difficult for the lemmings to find enough to eat. Traffic in the tunnels becomes more and more crowded, and the once friendly rodents no longer touch noses when they meet. Instead they claw and bite each other as they pass in the underground tunnels.

Finally the lemmings are unable to get along with each other. Tired of traffic tie-ups, and anxious for food, they decide to move. The only trouble is that there are so many of them, they cannot find a place to dig a new burrow. Squealing with rage, they mill about trying to find an unoccupied spot. It is impossible. There are too many lemmings.

Then suddenly an old male lemming, squeaking shrilly, sets out in a straight line. Like children playing follow-the-leader, most of the restless rodents fall in behind. They do not know where they are going. Nor do they care. Their only thought is to escape from the city.

As the brown stream flows along, it passes other lemming cities. Their inhabitants swell the flood, for they too feel the urge to migrate. Now there are millions of lemmings on the march. Birds of prey, bears, foxes, and wolves follow the column on wing and foot and devour great numbers of the marchers. But this is merely a ripple in the swelling tide that sweeps over everything in its path as it billows toward the sea.

The lemmings run up and down rocks, scramble through swamps, and swim across lakes and rivers. Many of them are eaten by fish. Worn out by the long journey, others drown. Their bodies pollute the water and, if it is used for drinking, cause a disease known as lemming fever. Farmers fear the invasion of "the mice from the sky," not only because the water supply is threatened, but also because the rodents eat their stored and growing crops. They can do nothing, however, to dam the torrent of lemmings that overflows their land.

At first migrating lemmings travel twenty-four hours a day. But once their cities are far behind, they move only at night. They stop at dawn to rest and feed. Sometimes they may spend several weeks in places where there is a large supply of food. During these stopovers, stragglers catch up to the main column. More young lemmings are born, and the population again increases in spite of the continued attacks of birds and other animals.

In a short time the food supplies are gone. The same crowded conditions that caused them to leave home in the first place are present. When this happens, the lemmings re-form their lines and again take up their march to the sea. Day and night they rush forward until they are too tired to go on. Those able to struggle to their feet continue the headlong flight, stopping once in a while but always heading for the seacoast. The migration may take two or three years, but at last the brown tide of lemmings sweeps onto the shore. It does not stop at the water's edge. The lemmings plunge in and head for the open sea.

Some scientists believe that the swimmers think the ocean is nothing but another body of water in their path. Others are of the opinion that the rodents are following a trail laid out by their ancestors thousands of years ago when there was dry land where now lie the Baltic and North Seas. Both groups are agreed, however, that the migrations are nature's way of keeping a proper balance between the rodent population and the food supply. For if most of the lemmings did not migrate, they would all die of hunger.

These ideas are not of the least concern to the lemmings. They are driven by a mysterious urge and paddle on and on until they sink beneath the waves.

Meanwhile, back in the uplands, the small number of lemmings that did not join the mad rush to the sea are very busy. They have families to raise and storerooms to stock. Life is very pleasant for these stay-at-homes. There is no crowding in the tunnels nor any difficulty in finding food. It will be four or five years before the underground cities again become overpopulated, and their furry inhabitants band together in another march of death.

Sigmund A. Lavine

Exploring Beyond the Story

 This is the story of a very strange migration. What does the word *migration* mean? Look in your glossary if you do not know. What is unusual about this particular migration?

Describe a lemming city. What do you think is one of the most interesting things about these cities? Why do lemmings leave their cities?

The lemming makes a march of death every few years. The salmon comes from the ocean and swims up a stream to the place where it was born. There it lays its eggs and dies. Read in an encyclopedia or science book of the strange habits of the eel, chameleon, green turtle, or some other animal of special interest to you. Be ready to report your findings to the group. Discuss how these habits harm or benefit the animals.

Understanding the Meaning

Explain what is meant by each of the following phrases. You may wish to reread the parts of the story from which they were taken to help you clarify the meanings.

> driven by a mysterious urge
> invasion of "the mice from the sky"
> nature's way of keeping a proper balance
> brown tide of lemmings sweeps onto the shore
> their inhabitants swell the flood
> anxious to gorge themselves

The author makes his story come alive by many interesting comparisons between the lives and habits of lemmings and of people. For example, he speaks of the traffic rush in the lemming cities. Skim the story to find other comparisons and list them so that you can discuss them with the group.

All But Blind

All but blind
  In his chambered hole
Gropes for worms
  The four-clawed Mole.

All but blind
  In the evening sky,
The hooded Bat
  Twirls softly by.

All but blind
  In the burning day
The Barn-Owl blunders
  On her way.

And blind as are
  These three to me,
So, blind to Someone
  I must be.

Walter de la Mare

Watchers of the Campfire

FOR FIVE YEARS the big panther who ruled the rough country around the headwaters of the Upsalquitch had been well content with his hunting ground. This winter, however, it had failed him. His tawny sides were thin. He longed for a full meal of deer or caribou. Occasionally he caught a rabbit to stay his hunger. But rabbits were a slim diet for such a large and hearty animal as he. There were few deer on the high plains and rough hills of the Upsalquitch, but the caribou had once thronged these plains. Now, without warning or excuse, they had vanished.

The panther was an old beast. He knew the caribou. He knew that without reason they would drift away to new pastures, often not so good as the ones they had left. Nevertheless, because the headwaters of the Upsalquitch were much to his liking, he had lingered there, awaiting their return. Now after a month of rabbits he too decided to leave this country. Perhaps if he moved westward he would come upon the trail of his lost herds.

At the end of a week of slow travel through heavy snow, the panther was still hungry. No caribou had crossed his trail. He had tried without luck to catch a beaver. And once he had dined on a fat porcupine, taking the creature by surprise and before it could loose its quills.

The very next day, about noon, he came across a trail, the first sight and scent of which brought the hair up along his backbone. The scent of the strange trail he knew and hated and feared. It was the man-scent.

The panther changed his direction and followed the man's trail at a rapid pace. Never before had his courage allowed him to trail a man. But this time was different. This time he was hungry, hungrier than he had ever been in his life before.

For some time he followed the trail at an easy lope. Now and then he would drop into a trot to rest himself. Occasionally he would stop and lie down for a few minutes.

At last, as twilight was gathering headway among the thickets, he was startled by a succession of sharp sounds just ahead of him. He stopped and crouched motionless in his tracks. Presently he recognized and understood the sharp sounds, especially when they were followed by a crackling and snapping of dry branches. He had heard them in the neighborhood of the lumber camps, before he had moved to the headwaters of the Upsalquitch. With understanding came new courage. He crept a little nearer, and from safe hiding watched the man at his task of gathering dry firewood for the night. From time to time the man looked about him, as if he felt himself watched. But he could not see the pale eyes that followed him unwinking from the depths of the thicket.

In a few minutes the panther saw the man take one of his heavy snowshoes and begin digging at the snow. Soon there was a round hole so deep that when the man stood up in it little more than his head and shoulders appeared over the edge. Then he carried in some of the wood which he had cut, together with a big armful of spruce boughs. He busied himself for a while at the bottom of the hole, his head appearing now and then, but only for a moment.

The panther watched, interested. Then, when it had grown so dark that he was about to steal from his hiding place and creep closer, there was a sudden flash of light, and smoke and flame arose from the hole. The panther, his lips twitching and his hair rising, shrank closer into his retreat.

The smoke and the scent of the burning sticks killed the scent of the man in the panther's nostrils. But presently there was a new scent, warm, rich, and appetizing. The panther did not know it, but he liked it. It was the smell of frying bacon. Seeing that the man was busy over the fire, the hungry beast

made a half circle of the campfire and noiselessly climbed a tree from which he could look down into the mysterious hole.

From his lookout he watched the man make his meal, smoke his pipe, build up the fire, and finally, rolling himself in his heavy blanket, settle himself for sleep. Then little by little the panther crept nearer. He feared the fire. But the fire soon began to die down, and the panther crept out upon a massive hemlock limb, almost overlooking the hole, but screened by a veil of fine green branches. From this post he could spring upon the sleeper at one bound. That is, he could as soon as his courage was big enough. He feared the man, even asleep. But little by little he began to realize that he feared his own hunger more. Lower and lower sank the dying fire. The sleeper slept unstirring. And so the panther, equally unstirring, watched.

105

A little beyond the campfire rose the slopes of a wooded ridge. The ridge was covered with a heavy second growth of birch, maple, Canada fir, and white spruce. The ancient forest had fallen years before under the axes of lumbermen. Here on the ridge, where the food they loved was plentiful, a buck with his herd of does and fawns had established his winter "yard."

The little herd which roamed this particular yard chanced to be feeding very near the foot of the ridge when suddenly a faint red glow, stealing through the branches, caught the buck's eye. There was a quick stamp of warning, and the herd turned to statues, their faces all one way, their sensitive ears, quivering nostrils, and wide eyes all striving to understand this strange red glow. They were a herd from the deep woods. Not one of them had ever been near the settlements. Not even the wise old leader had ever seen a fire. This light, when the sun had set and no moon held the sky, was strange indeed.

To the deer, a mystery means something to be solved. He has the dangerous gift of curiosity. After only a few minutes of motionless watching, the whole herd began noiselessly moving toward the strange light. At the smell of the frying bacon, they stopped again. Very soon they continued their cautious advance.

At last they came to a spot where their keen eyes could see the hole in the snow, the campfire, and the man seated beside it. At this point the old buck decided they had seen enough and gave the signal to leave. The whole herd turned obediently, all but one young doe.

Step by step she continued along till she came to the campfire. Then, planting herself in the snow, her gray body hidden in the shadows beyond the campfire, her wide eyes watched the man. She saw him roll himself into his blanket. Then she stood quietly, watching the fire.

* * *

Very early that same morning a chopper in the lumber camp had started out on his snowshoes for a two days' tramp to the settlements. Though not a hunter, the man was a skilled woodsman. He knew the woods and the wildlife that lived there. He had no wish to kill these wild things, great or small. Yet he was a famous marksman, and he always carried a rifle on his long tramps to the settlements.

He carried the rifle because of stories he had heard in the camps. The stories were about panthers. Some said they were extinct in New Brunswick. Others insisted they were still around. To be on the safe side, the man carried his rifle.

On this particular day he had traveled all the morning without adventure. During the afternoon he was once or twice surprised by a creepy feeling along his backbone and in the roots of his hair. He stopped and peered about him carefully, with a feeling that he was followed. But he saw only woods and snow without even a track across it.

When he had gathered his firewood and dug the hole for his camp and stopped to build his campfire, he felt again that he was being watched. The feeling was stronger than ever, so when he at last settled himself for sleep, he made sure his rifle was within reach of his hand.

He had been asleep only a short while when something woke him. There was no sound in the snow-still woods, and he thought it must have been a dream that pulled him out of his tired sleep. Without moving and with half-opened eyes, he peered into the dark around him. The campfire was throwing some light into the thickets near him, and his eyes searched them. Suddenly his body stiffened under its blanket. Two big round shining eyes were gazing at him through a tangle of spruce boughs. In a moment he saw growing up around the eyes the head of a deer. He smiled in the dark and settled back. Was it only the steady gaze of this harmless creature which had jerked him awake? He let his eyes wander upward to the hemlock bough stretching almost over his camp bed. In the glow from the fire he plainly saw the outline of the panther and the two gleaming coals of its eyes!

He knew better than to reach for his rifle. He knew that the least movement would be the signal for the panther to leap down upon him. There was nothing to do but wait and keep perfectly still, and think.

The passing minutes seemed hours. Just when the man thought he could bear the waiting no longer, a stick in the fire burned through and fell, sending up a shower of sparks. The panther drew back and shifted his gaze for a moment, and in that moment the man reached for his gun.

But not only the panther had been startled by the falling stick and the shower of sparks. The young doe had given a startled leap away from the camp, thus catching the panther's eye.

Softly, softly the great beast drew back along the hemlock bough and started to climb down. Deer were more in his line than human kind. He was not afraid to hunt deer.

The man thought quickly. Panthers were indeed very few in New Brunswick and interesting as part of the region's wildlife. But the man loved the deer, and to this particular deer he felt he perhaps owed his life.

As the panther turned to slip down the hemlock's trunk, the man sat up straight. He took careful aim at a point just behind the panther's shoulder. At the report of the rifle the great body fell limp.

The man sprang to his feet and stirred the campfire to a blaze. And the doe, her heart pounding with panic, went crashing off through the bushes.

Charles G. D. Roberts

Thinking About the Story

Within this story are three smaller stories about a panther, a deer, and a man. These three meet at the campfire. Tell how the panther, the deer, and the man each happened to be at this particular place. Who were the watchers of the campfire?

What gave the panther courage to trail man whom he hated and feared? List the phrases or words used by the author to tell the reader that the panther was hungry.

At the end of the story the man has to make a quick decision. What two things did he consider before making it? Do you think he did the right thing? Why?

Learning More About the Story Setting

On a map of Canada locate New Brunswick and the Upsalquitch River. In a geography or an encyclopedia find out more about the country described in the story. What sections of the United States are similar to it? Might a person encounter the animals described in the story in these sections?

Compare the characters and the setting of "Hunting the Haunt Fox" and "Watchers of the Campfire." How are they alike? How are they different?

Saying It Another Way

Be ready to explain the following phrases in your own words. To whom is the author referring in each one?

    ruled the rough country
    a creepy feeling along his backbone and in the roots
        of his hair
    crashing off through the bushes
    shrank closer into his retreat

Buffalo Dusk

The buffaloes are gone.
And those who saw the buffaloes are gone.
Those who saw the buffaloes by thousands and
    how they pawed the prairie sod into dust
    with their hoofs, their great heads down
    pawing on in a great pageant of dusk,
Those who saw the buffaloes are gone.
And the buffaloes are gone.

Carl Sandburg

The River Crossing

THE FLOCK drifted forward in the warmth of midmorning sun. It browsed in slow, shifting, seeming uncertain movement as small bunches fell behind and then moved forward to overtake the others. Out on the two sides trotted the two dogs and stopped to sit on haunches, with tongues panting, and trotted forward again. Behind walked Old Ramon, swinging his stick in rhythm with his long slow strides, and following him walked the boy, leading the burro.

"I think," said the boy, "that the tending of the sheep means a muchness of walking in the sun."

"It means that," said Old Ramon. "Always it is so on a journeying. But when we are in the hills, there will be the shade of the bigger trees and the days of sitting still. Of Ramon sitting still and watching the sheep put on good flesh and grow good wool and thinking of the many years of his living. And I think that he will be watching a boy play boy-games with a dog. . . ."

The flock drifted forward, and the ground sloped away to a far-off curving line of reddish willow brush-clumps and a few big cottonwoods.

"And now we must cross that little river," said Old Ramon. "And we must have care. There is nothing that shows the stupidness of the sheep and of the flock like the water. I have known a flock that went almost mad with the thirst because it would not drink from a pool, the one pool for many miles around, and good water, that a strange flock had visited and left there its smell. And yet at another pool that another strange flock had visited, it might drink with no noticing. I have heard of flocks that lost many dead sheep because they

broke away and could not be stopped and ran to water that everyone knows is bad. And when one must cross the water— ai, then there is no knowing. Perhaps the flock will cross as if it is a nothing, a little splashing in the water and that is all. Perhaps it will refuse and turn back and make the trouble. There is a good crossing here, not wide but good, where the water is not too fast and not too deep. But there is no knowing. . . ."

Old Ramon stopped and leaned on his stick. "It is time. Now call your dog to you."

The boy put two fingers in his mouth and whistled and his young black dog leaped around and come bounding to him.

"Good," said Old Ramon. "But you must teach him about the whistling. One time is to look, to see what is wanted. Two is to come. . . . Now fasten the burro to that bush and wait here. You will see how Ramon and his Pedro have care at a crossing."

Old Ramon strode forward, swinging his stick to match long strides, and as he strode, he put two fingers in his mouth and whistled and the brown dog stopped and looked back. Old Ramon swung his right arm out in a sweeping gesture around and back to his chest. The brown dog raced forward and in front of the flock, between it and the low sloping near-edge of the little river that was about fifty feet away, and stopped the leaders and raced back and forth, holding the flock there as the stragglers moved up crowding in from behind. Old Ramon strode to the front of the flock and with his stick reached and pushed and prodded and cut out forward six sheep and herded these toward the water. The rest of the flock was bunched in close order now, intent, those in front standing motionless, legs braced against jostling from behind, staring, watching.

The brown dog swung away from them, leaving them standing braced and staring in their silly way, and raced to help Old Ramon. The six sheep were at the water's edge, sniffing at the shallow swift current that rolled noisily over small rocks and pebbles. They pulled back from it and tried to turn away.

"Ai," said Old Ramon. "They would be stubborn today"

One of the sheep at the water's edge broke away, and the old dog, a streak of dark brown against the pink-tan of the ground, headed it and brought it back. The rest of the flock stood and stared and watched. Gently, gently, but firmly, Old Ramon and the brown dog pressed and prodded the six sheep to face toward the water again. Suddenly Old Ramon raised his right hand and pointed at one of the sheep, at Juanita, and the brown dog lunged forward and leaped upon her hindquarters. His weight pushed her into the water. She stumbled and caught her footing and moved ahead, and Old Ramon pointed again, and another was in the water, and the others moved forward, following.

Old Ramon strode into the water that swirled about his legs to the knees and urged the sheep forward. Juanita pulled herself dripping out on the other low sloping bank and moved on, seeming to forget in the instant the water just past and still dripping from her, already dropping her head in search of forage, and the others followed.

Old Ramon strode back to the near bank, and already the brown dog was racing to the rest of the flock, swinging in at the side of those in front to start them moving. There was little need for urging. The flock saw the six on the opposite bank and wanted to be with them and moved forward, the first stepping into the water as if it were a nothing, and the others following. And Old Ramon on the one side and the brown dog on the other side pressed them inwards, funneling them down to the crossing.

Back up the sloping the boy stood and watched, and the black dog crouched quivering and eager by his feet. "We must stay here," said the boy. "That is what we were told." He stood straight and looked out at the flock, the three hundred sheep flowing forward in a wide stream that narrowed down to the crossing, and at an old man and old brown dog working together, silent and intent, in the swift sureness of knowledge and the years.

There were stragglers at the rear of the flock, the late ones, the slow movers, the always behind. The boy saw Old Ramon wave at him to bring them forward.

"It is our turn, Sancho," said the boy, and ran toward the stragglers. The black dog, eager and anxious, bounded ahead and nipped at flanks, and the stragglers jumped, startled, and hurried after the flock.

But the black dog, too eager, too anxious, too excited, began barking wildly and nipping harder, and the stragglers broke into the bunched rear of the flock that had not crossed the river. These, startled in turn, began to scatter and run to the sides along the bank. Some pressed forward in desperation and crowded those in the water, and there was floundering and frantic scramblings on the uncertain footing of the river bottom.

"Ai!" shouted Old Ramon. Blood rushed into his scarred bandit face. Anger shook his voice. "That fool! Hold him!"

The boy ran, calling, grabbing, and caught hold of the black dog and crouched with his fists tight in the thick fur of the dog's neck. He looked up and saw Old Ramon hurrying, hurrying, leaping on tireless old legs and with reaching stick, and the old dog a brown streak here and there and everywhere, the two of them heading, turning, gathering the scattered sheep, and herding them to the crossing.

"Ai! Ai!" cried Old Ramon.

Two sheep had been crowded and jostled down in the river and carried by their own floundering and by the current downstream into a pool. There, silent in the way of sheep in danger, they struggled in the water, their heads bobbing up as their forefeet flailed under the surface, but with the weight of the water soaking into their fleeces, pulling them down.

Old Ramon dropped his stick and threw off his hat and ran to the pool. With long strides he strode into it. The water rose to his waist, to his shoulders. He had one of the sheep and pushed it through the water ahead of him to the opposite bank, and as he heaved from behind, it pulled itself out. He turned back for the other. Only its nose showed. He came to it and ducked down out of sight in the water and

straightened with his right shoulder under the sheep and heaved and struggled toward the bank. He worked along the bank to its lowest point with the sheep hanging limp over his shoulder and heaved it out on the dry ground and crawled out after it. Still on his knees he turned the sheep so that its head lay down the slope. Its eyes were closed and water trickled from its mouth. He worked over it with big knobbed knowing hands. More water trickled from its mouth and its eyes opened and its head moved and its legs began to kick in little jerks and suddenly it scrambled to its feet and staggered some sideways and moved away.

Old Ramon rose to his feet. His breath came in great gasps. Water dripped from all of him and muddied the ground around his heavy old boots. He looked toward the flock. It grazed along the slope from the river to the level beyond and it was shaped into a flock again. The two sheep from the pool were joining it, and in front of it an old brown dog stood guard, holding it there, waiting. Old Ramon moved his head to the side. Fifteen feet away the boy stood, straight and still. His legs were wet from the river. In one hand he held the lead rope of the burro and in the other Old Ramon's hat and stick. At his feet crouched the black dog, in fear and shame.

"Ai!" said Old Ramon between gasps. "I was the fool—to bring that fool!"

"We are sorry," said the boy. He stood a little straighter. "But he is like me. He has to learn."

"To learn!" said Old Ramon. "It must be born—in the dog—as in the man!"

The boy looked down at the ground by his feet. His shoulders sagged a bit, and he seemed to shrink smaller. He kicked at the ground with one foot and did not look up. "I will take him back," he said. "I will carry food and follow the way we came. We are only nuisances that get in the way of your work."

Old Ramon stood still, very still except for the movement of his chest seeking breath. He turned his head and looked on down the little river where it flowed into the distances of the big land and was lost around the curve of a far low ridge. The last drops dripped from him, and the warm sun dried those on his face, and still he stood looking into the distances of the big land.

"Ai," he said softly. "I am old. I forget what it is to be young."

Old Ramon strode over to the boy. He took his hat and plopped it at a jaunty angle on his head. He took his stick and thumped it on the ground and leaned on it. "We will have no more foolish talk about nuisances. What is a little splashing in the water? It is a bathing. There are those who say that never does a sheepman have a bathing, an all-over washing, except when a sheep falls into the water and he must pull it out. I think it is that now Ramon has had a good bathing." He turned toward the flock and put two fingers in his mouth and whistled, once, twice, and the brown dog started around the flock and trotted toward him. He turned again to the boy and pointed with his stick at an angle up the long low sloping from the river. "Do you see that mesa rising there to the southwest?"

"I see it," said the boy.

"That is the way we are going. Straight toward it and then around it to the left."

The brown dog had come close now and sat back on its haunches and looked up at Old Ramon.

"Pedro," said Old Ramon, pointing at the boy. "That one will be your master for a time. You will do as he directs."

The boy stood straighter, staring at Old Ramon.

"But—but I do not understand."

Old Ramon reached to take the lead rope from the boy's hand. "I think that the way to learn is to do. You will take the flock as I told you. You and my Pedro and your Sancho. You will start the flock in the right direction and push it, gently, gently. I will sit here and pour from my boots the water I feel around my toes, and perhaps I will rest for a moment. And then I will follow."

The boy stood straight and still. He saw that the brown dog looked now at him. He saw Old Ramon holding the stick out toward him. He took the stick. He was not tall enough to lean with his hands on the rounded knob at the top, but he took hold lower down and leaned on it. He looked at the brown dog and nodded his head, and the brown dog trotted away toward the flock, and the black dog, seeing the others move, bounded after but did not bound ahead and stayed behind and followed. The boy too started away, swinging the stick in rhythm with slow strides.

Old Ramon wrapped the lead rope of the burro around one wrist and sat down on the slope of the river bank and tugged at one old boot. "Ai," he said softly. "I am the fool. I forget. . . ."

Jack Schaefer

Taking Another Look

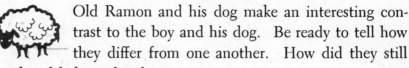

Old Ramon and his dog make an interesting contrast to the boy and his dog. Be ready to tell how they differ from one another. How did they still need and help each other?

Why was it necessary to take such great care when crossing the river with the flock? Find and be ready to read aloud the part in which Old Ramon explains this to the boy.

What are some things the author tells us about the care of sheep? Why were they journeying to the hills?

Ramon, the boy, and Sancho each learned a lesson. What did each one learn?

Finding Words That Describe

At the beginning of the story the author gives us a feeling of peace and ease of movement. List some of the words that suggest a quiet setting.

When trouble begins, the mood changes. What are some words that suggest the excitement and confusion?

Animals at Home

IMAGINE THE THRILL of being able to see the greatest variety of wild animals ever gathered in one place, at liberty, living their natural lives unharmed by man. It is something which must be seen to be believed.

The Kruger National Park, or Game Reserve, is where all these creatures may be seen. It was made possible by a gift of land to the people of South Africa from their famous leader, Paul Kruger. He deeply loved wildlife and hoped by this gift of land to save his country's unusual and beautiful animals from harm and final destruction.

The Reserve covers about eight thousand square miles of the Transvaal, in the Republic of South Africa. It is divided into rest camps, made up of groups of houses built around a clubhouse. Each camp is in charge of a game warden.

These camps lie within easy distance of each other and make it possible for the visitor to stay in different parts of the Park. In this way he can see the animals in the particular region which is their natural home. Some camps are inside a high stockade and are entered through a huge double-barred gate. The Reserve is crisscrossed by over a thousand miles of trails and roads, the main roads leading from camp to camp.

The visitor, arriving at one of the main gates, is registered and directed to stay at one or other of the camps. He is inspected for firearms, which are not allowed, while a friendly warden explains that there is one never-to-be-broken law of the Reserve. One may travel only by car, and no matter what happens, one may not get out of it, not even to fix a tire, or to take a better "close-up" photograph.

"But if the car breaks down, or has a flat tire, how do we get back?" we ask nervously, our minds filled with pictures of hungry lions or angry rhinoceros.

"You just wait until you're rescued," is the prompt answer.

It is explained that every car is registered in each camp, with the time, destination, and expected return listed. Each returning car is again checked. If one is missing, the warden and guards responsible for it set off to find it.

The reason for this never-to-be-broken rule is perhaps not very plain to those who do not know much of African wildlife. Almost no animal, except perhaps an enraged rhinoceros or elephant, will charge a car. Those that might attack man to protect their young do not get his scent behind the much stronger scent of gasoline. As long as one remains inside the car, the animals fear no danger. The Game Reserve has no record of a *parked* car ever being attacked, even though full of nervous visitors longing to be rescued!

We left our entrance gate as the afternoon light began to slant through the trees and the long golden grass. We were given directions for the road to our camp and stern warnings

126

not to travel at more than ten or fifteen miles an hour. This is especially important for fear that any animals crossing the road be frightened, particularly lions. Lions love to trot along the open trails and take a dust bath in dusty patches on the roads.

Once inside the high gates of our camp, our car was parked at the side of the club building. There we were given two little houses and a servant to help us.

We had dinner at the clubhouse. After dinner we wandered about inside the stockade. We were comforted that it looked strong enough to keep out any prowler. We were alive to the silence that falls with the African night. Then we began to listen closely, excitedly, as we realized the silence was actually full of sounds made by the wildlife all around us. Suddenly the air was torn by the long, haunting howl of a hyena, echoing across the veld. We shivered and hurried inside, seeking the comfort of our beds.

127

Animals are awake and about with the first light, so the only time to see them is either very early, or as darkness falls. They rest in the shadows throughout the hot hours of the day, and it is then that their coloring protects them best. They become part of their sunlit, shadow-flecked world and are impossible to see.

So we were up before dawn, while the sky was still a dark sapphire bowl, edged with green along the horizon. Our servant brought us steaming coffee, and we filled our thermos bottles for a second breakfast later in the car.

We were told that there had been a "kill" that night, and if we wanted particularly to see lions, this was our chance. So, following directions, we set off at a slow speed along the sandy trail leading from our camp into the unknown.

Almost at once we seemed to be among the animals. Some were grazing peacefully near the roadside. Others farther away could hardly be seen in the dim light.

128

We disturbed a herd of zebra, grazing with their ugly friends the wildebeest, who so often are with them. The long, sad face of the wildebeest under the cowlike horns, the wiry beard and tail give it a queer, unnatural look. But it is a fierce fighter and a cautious traveler, keen of sight and scent. This animal is always on guard while grazing, for its meat is much liked by the lion.

Our road ran along the base of a low stony hill, and all at once we seemed to be surrounded by the monkey people. They were actually baboons of all sizes and ages. There were big, powerful males glaring at us from some "outpost" and babies clinging to their mothers. We were afraid their barks would warn all other animals of our coming, so we turned off the motor and waited in silence.

After a little while we moved slowly over the brow of the hill and saw that all our hopes were realized. Only a few yards from the roadside lay a fresh-killed zebra, being devoured by what might truly be called a "pride of lion." We counted eight lions—five females and three huge males.

We drove forward very slowly so as not to disturb the group, and were so interested in the scene that we were hardly aware of a huge lion and his mate approaching. They crossed the road just a yard or two in front of our car, which we had again stopped, with motor silent. The pair seemed quite unaware of us, though we gasped in surprise as the "king of beasts" strode past the hood of the car toward the "kill."

From another direction three more lions appeared. We seemed to be surrounded by the animals and sat, frozen, breathless with excitement, as one lioness stopped to sniff our front wheels, and gazed through the window at us with a cold, golden-eyed stare.

The next day we set out for fresh adventures in another part of the Reserve. We had decided to visit a well-known pool in one of the rivers running through the park, where the hippopotamus lived.

On our drive, we passed numbers of different antelopes named after the places where they are found. All the horns of the antelopes are beautifully shaped. That of the impala ram is perhaps the most beautiful. This buck is famous for its speed and surprising agility. It will leap this way and that, sometimes ten to fifteen feet at a stretch.

A herd of impala racing across a high horizon is like a flock of strange birds in low, wavy flight. We watched an excited herd leap right across the road only a few yards ahead of us. They formed a perfect arch of living animals in easy effortless bounds.

And then suddenly we saw the giraffes, the "spotted skyscrapers of the veld," in a group, nibbling the topmost shoots of the tall acacia trees. Their long necks curved among the branches, dark against the skyline. They were not far from the road.

We were able to watch the motherly attentions given to a calf by one of the cows. She kept nudging her baby forward to the more appetizing growth within his reach. Giraffes are shy animals, and sensing our nearness, they soon disappeared over the rising ground, the calf carefully protected by his parents.

The Reserve is full of game birds, but except for the wild guinea fowl often met along the roadside, they are too shy to be seen. At sunrise and sunset, however, the air is full of bird calls.

131

We approached the bridge across the river with added care, for here we had been warned we would be met by a guide and allowed to leave our car. Under his protection, we hoped we might be lucky enough to find a hippo still on land, and sleepy from his night's rest in the tall grass along the banks.

The guide greeted us with his finger to his lips. Tense with excitement, we followed him, creeping as silently as possible along a pathway between the trees.

Suddenly the guide stopped and pointed into a thicket of high reeds just ahead of us. He motioned us to follow, approaching the spot against the wind. But the sharp ears and keen noses of the hippos warned them and, with loud snorts, they shuffled into the water before we could properly see them.

We followed their path to the river's edge as quickly as we could, and there we could see only the tiny, alert ears of the huge animals sticking out of the water. The hippo has a large bump of curiosity. Even when scenting danger, he will raise his head enough above water to take a quick glance at anything strange or unexpected on the bank.

The shallower waters of the pool were covered with blue water hyacinths. One hippo had pushed his head up through the hyacinths, so that a wreath of the flowers trailed over the humorous face of the creature. We laughed at the funny picture he made, whereupon the hippo plunged, outraged by our amusement, only to appear again ten feet away to watch us out of one cocked eye.

Each day in the Kruger National Park brings some exciting adventure. As man takes over more of the earth's surface, destroying nature as he moves along, a game reserve such as this one becomes of greater value to us all.

Jan Juta

132

Thinking About the Story

This story tells about a most unusual game reserve. Why is this game reserve of great value? Tell something about the Kruger National Park or Game Reserve. Where is it located? How large is it? How are the animals that live there protected?

Who was Paul Kruger? Why did he give the land for this Reserve? If there is a game reserve in the region where you live, tell the group about it.

Explain the never-to-be-broken law of the Reserve and be ready to tell the reason for having this law.

Using Words That Describe

The author by his vivid descriptions creates a feeling for the beauty of the African night. Explain the following sentences in your own words:

We were alive to the silence that falls with the African night.

The sky was still a dark sapphire bowl, edged with green along the horizon.

The author describes some of the animals in a humorous way. Who are the "spotted skyscrapers?" What is meant by the statement, "The hippo has a large bump of curiosity?" There is another humorous description of the hippo in this story. Be prepared to read it aloud to the class.

Exploring Beyond the Story

Skim the story and make a list of all the animals mentioned. Write a brief report about one of these animals. Use the encyclopedia to get the information you need for the report. Make an illustration of the animal you have chosen.

The Hippopotamus

In the squdgy river,
  Down the oozely bank,
Where the ripples shiver,
  And the reeds are rank

Where the purple Kippo
  Makes an awful fuss,
Lives the hip-hip-hippo
  Hippo-pot-a-mus!

Broad his back and steady;
  Broad and flat his nose;
Sharp and keen and ready
  Little eyes are those.

You would think him dreaming
  Where the mud is deep.
It is only seeming—
  He is not asleep.

Better not disturb him,
  There'd be an awful fuss
If you touched the Hippo,
  Hippo-pot-a-mus.

          Georgia Roberts Durston

Friends in Books

King of the Wind

IN THE northwestern slice of Africa known as Morocco, a horseboy stood, with broom in hand, in the vast courtyard of the royal stables of the Sultan. He was waiting for dusk to fall.

All day long he had eaten nothing, for this was the sacred month of Ramadan when, day after day, all faithful Mohammedans neither eat nor drink from the dawn before sunrise until the moment after sunset.

The boy Agba had not minded the fast for himself. It was part of his religion. But when Signor Achmet, Chief of the Grooms, commanded that the horses, too, observe the fast, Agba's dark eyes smouldered with anger.

"It is the order of the Sultan!" the Signor had announced to the horseboys. And he had cuffed Agba on the head when the boy showed his disapproval.

Of the twelve thousand horses in the Sultan's stables, Agba had charge of ten. He fed and watered them and polished their coats and cleaned their stalls. Best of all, he wheeled the whole string into the courtyard at one time for their exercise.

136

To one of the ten horses Agba had lost his heart. She was a bay mare, as fleet as a gazelle, with eyes that studied him in whatever he did. The other nine horses he would lead out to the common water trough to drink. But for his bright bay he would fill a water cask from a pure spring beyond the palace gates. Then he would hold it while the mare sucked the water, her eyelashes brushing his fingers as she drank.

137

It was the mare that worried Agba now as he worked to fill in the time until the hour of sunset. The courtyard was already swept clean, but Agba pushed his palm-leaf broom as if he were sweeping all his thoughts into a little mound for the wind to carry away.

At last he hung his broom on an iron hook, alongside an endless row of brooms, and went to the mare. Her stall door was closed so that the fragrance of late clover would not drift in to prick her appetite. He found her asleep, lying on her side, her great belly distended by the little colt soon to be born. Agba noticed, with a heavy feeling in his chest, that the fast was telling on the mare. He could read it in the sunken places above each eye, in the harshness of her coat.

But soon the fast would be over. It was the last day of the month, and even now the sun was sinking below the gray-green olive trees that surrounded the courtyard.

Agba turned toward the east, his eyes on the minaret of the mosque. It was a sharp needle pricking the blood-red reflection of the sun. He gazed fixedly at it until his eyes smarted. At last a figure in white robes emerged from the tower. It was the public crier, sounding his trumpet, crying four times to the four winds of heaven. The fast of Ramadan was at an end!

The air went wild with noise. Horseboys swarmed out of the corridors and into the courtyard.

Agba did not join the other horseboys. He returned to the mare. He reached under the saddle hung on the wall and found the water vessel he had filled and hidden there an hour ago. He poured the water into a basin and waited for the mare to awaken.

As if she had heard the sound of the water, she woke with a jerk and struggled to her feet. She came to Agba and drank.

When he came out of the mare's stall, the other boys were beginning to lead their horses to the common trough to drink. Agba must hurry now if he hoped to get his corn ration first. He picked up a bag made of hemp and ran through many corridors and down a steep staircase to the underground granary. At the entrance stood Signor Achmet, Chief of the Grooms. Signor Achmet was dark and bearded. In his right hand he carried a knotted stick, and at his waist hung a hundred keys.

"Why do you not eat with the other slave boys?" he asked when he saw Agba.

Agba gulped. He studied his brown toes.

"Is it the mare?"

The boy's eyes flew to the Signor's.

"Is tonight her hour?"

Slowly, gravely, Agba nodded.

"Tonight, then," the Signor said, "tonight you will move the mare into the brood-mare stable. You will remain on watch and call me when she is ready to foal."

The new moon hung over Agba's shoulder as he ran to get the mare. She was standing patiently in a corner of her stall, her head lowered, her tail tucked in. Placing a hand on her neck, Agba led her out into the night. She walked slowly, heavily.

She entered the stall. She tried the soft bed of straw with her feet. She went to the manger. Her nose quivered at the smell of the dried grasses, but she did not eat. She put her lips to the water cask but did not drink. At last she tucked her hooves underneath her, and with a groan lay down. Her head began to nod. She steadied it in the straw. Then her breathing, too, steadied.

With a sigh Agba sank down in the straw. At last he, too, slept, but his was a deep sleep. The candle in the lantern hanging on the wall flickered and died. The new moon rode higher and higher.

With the gray light of morning he woke with a start. There was the mare lying on her side as before. But her head was raised now, and she was drying off a newborn foal! How tiny the foal was! And so wet there was no telling what its color would be. But its eyes were open. And they were full of curiosity.

Quivering with wonder and afraid to move, Agba watched the mare clumsily get to her feet. He watched her nudge the young thing with her nose.

"I could carry him in my arms," thought Agba. "He is not much bigger than a goat. And he is all of one color. Except —except . . ." Suddenly the boy's heart missed a beat. On the off hind heel there was a white spot. It was no bigger than an almond, but it was there! The white spot—the sign of swiftness!

140

Agba knew he should be reporting to Signor Achmet. He knew he should be standing in line for his measure of corn. But he could not bear to break the spell. He listened to the colt suckling, to the mare munching the dried grasses. He smelled their warm bodies. A stable was a *good* place to be born.

Agba's thoughts were brought up sharply. The door to the stall was opening silently, and Signor Achmet was standing over him, an angry light in his eyes.

Agba sprang to his feet, waiting for the tongue-lashing, waiting for the bony fingers on his shoulder.

But the eyes of the Signor were no longer on him. The groom was examining the foal's chest, his face frozen in horror. He was shoving the mare aside to look closer. At last he spoke three words and each fell with a ping, like hail on a roof top: *"The wheat ear!"*

Agba came as close as he dared. He bent low so that he, too, could see the foal's chest. And there, just as the groom had said, was a cross-graining of hairs closely resembling a ripened beard of wheat.

141

"The wheat ear!" Signor Achmet's voice broke. "It foretells evil. Ill luck will attend the colt's days. Ill luck will hang low over the royal stables."

His eyes fixed on the foal's chest, he got slowly to his feet, drawing the saber at his belt.

Agba smothered a cry. Unmindful of his own safety, he thrust himself between Signor Achmet and the foal. He fell to his knees, lifting the tiny foal whose legs beat a tattoo in the air. With a look of triumph he pointed to the white spot on the off hind heel.

Signor Achmet's eyes narrowed. His brows came together in a black line. Agba could see him weighing the two in his mind—the white spot against the wheat ear. The good sign against the bad. The scales tipped even.

Grudgingly the groom sheathed his saber. "But the mare's milk will give the colt no strength," he added quickly. "She will die. It is the will of Allah."

The groom's prediction came true. In spite of Agba's care, the bay mare lived only a few days after the birth of her colt. When the Signor heard about it, he came thudding in his yellow sandals to the mare's stall. He made another prediction.

"The foal will die too," he said, shrugging his bony shoulders. "There is nothing to be done. Go to your quarters. Begone!"

Agba ran out of the stall. He took no notice of anyone. He did not know where he was going. He only knew that he wanted to run until he could run no more—away from death and life. He ran out the gates and down the hill to the city.

"Some evil spirit must be after him," the shopkeepers said and laughed to one another.

On and on Agba went, half-blinded by his tears, until suddenly he was almost knocked flat by the saddle trappings of a camel.

He stopped and stared. The camel was followed by her calf. A thought startled Agba. *Camel's milk!* Horses of the desert were often raised on it. He had heard Signor Achmet say it was better than mare's milk. Stronger. Richer.

He ran to the driver, pulling the hem of his mantle to attract his attention. The driver turned around angrily. At once he recognized Agba. The boy had often been sent to him to buy

camel skins for making stirrup leathers. Agba was the Signor's favorite errand boy. The driver's scowl turned into a greedy smile. But his smile became a frightened squawk when Agba fell in a little heap at his feet. The driver dismounted and began fanning the boy. A crowd quickly gathered. They were full of words.

"The fast of Ramadan has weakened him."

"We saw him running beyond his strength."

"He is the first slave boy of the Sultan's groom."

"He needs food and water."

The camel driver stopped his fanning. He took one of the many goatskin bags from the camel's load, untied a drinking vessel, and poured out some of the precious camel's milk he was taking to market to sell. He must save this small boy from the royal stables. It might bring him good fortune in the end.

He put the cup to Agba's lips and the boy drank a little, then more. When he had finished, the driver gave the boy a whole goatskin sack of the milk. There would be time enough later to find out what the Signor had wanted of him.

"Go back now," he urged, "before the sun climbs higher. Sleep. Whatever your message, it can wait."

Agba went straight to the colt's stall. He slipped inside and quietly closed the door behind him. The colt was still there! He was lying on his side, breathing lightly. He was alive, but oh, how thin and weak he was!

Agba took the goatskin sack from inside his shirt where he had held it close against his body to keep the milk warm. He filled a cup with it, then knelt beside the colt. He stirred the milk with his fingers and slid them into the colt's mouth. The colt sucked them, weak at first, then fiercely. Agba dipped his fingers again and again. He had never known such happiness

before. He made little purring noises in his throat. He made all sorts of promises in his mind. "My name is Agba. *Ba* means father. I will be a father to you, little one. When you are grown the multitudes will bow before you. And you will be King of the Wind."

Marguerite Henry

Agba's promise to the colt was kept. Through many countries and after many hardships, the colt was to prove his fleetness and courage. He would found a line of race horses which would produce the greatest thoroughbreds of all time, among them Man o' War.

The whole story of Agba and the Godolphin Arabian, as the colt became known, is told by Marguerite Henry in King of the Wind. *It's a book you won't want to miss.*

Thinking About the Story

Agba was more concerned for a horse than he was for himself. Why was he worried about the horse? How did he care for it? Was he required to give it so much attention? Why did he do so?

Explain the two important discoveries which were made about the new colt. Why was the colt's life spared?

The Signor made two predictions. What was the first one? Did it come true? Tell about the second prediction.

How did Agba suddenly get an idea for helping the colt? By what strange turn of events did Agba get what he wanted for the colt without even asking for it? Why did the camel driver help Agba?

Why didn't the second prediction come true? What promise did Agba make to the colt? Agba, too, made a prediction. What was it? Write a paragraph explaining how this prediction came true.

Saying It Another Way

Below are some of the author's phrases and sentences that give vivid word pictures of the action and feeling of the story. Explain each one in your own words.

> a sharp needle pricking the blood-red reflection of
>   the sun
> wheeled the whole string
> as fleet as a gazelle
> prick her appetite
> a heavy feeling in his chest
> The new moon hung over Agba's shoulder.

Find and be ready to read other descriptive phrases that are used by the author.

The Blood Horse

Gamarra is a dainty steed,
Strong, black, and of a noble breed,
Full of fire, and full of bone,
All his line of fathers known;
Fine his nose, his nostrils thin,
But blown abroad by the pride within!
His mane, a stormy river flowing,
And his eyes like embers glowing
In the darkness of the night,
And his pace as swift as light.

Barry Cornwall

Tommy Stubbins Meets Doctor Dolittle

Doctor Dolittle is one of the best loved people in the whole world of children's books. Boys and girls first met this famous character in a book called The Story of Doctor Dolittle, *by Hugh Lofting, in which they learned about his ability to understand the speech of animals. It is not unusual for a person to understand the speech of parrots. But it is not every day that one meets a man who knows exactly what a cat or a dog or even a monkey is saying. And Doctor Dolittle did.*

He lived differently from most people too. He had a duck, Dab-Dab, who kept house for him. And one of his very special friends was the dog Jip. Jip was not only the Doctor's trusted companion, but he was a helper too. He fed the large number of animals that shared Doctor Dolittle's house whenever the doctor was called away from home. And Jip helped Dab-Dab in the house too. Once Jip and Doctor Dolittle traveled all the way to Africa to help the monkeys there. They were ever so grateful and never forgot the doctor's kindness.

The story which follows is told by Tommy Stubbins, a boy who once lived in the same town as did Doctor Dolittle. It is the story of how Tommy met the doctor for the first time and it is told in Tommy's own words.

ONE MORNING early in the spring among the hills back of the town, I happened to come upon a hawk with a squirrel in its claws. The hawk was so frightened when I came upon it suddenly like this, that it dropped the poor creature and flew away. I picked the squirrel up and found that two of its legs were badly hurt. So I carried it in my arms back to the town.

When I came to the bridge, I went into the mussel-man's hut and asked him if he could do anything for it. Joe put on his spectacles and examined it carefully. Then he shook his head.

"There be only one man I know who could save yon crittur's life. And that's John Dolittle."

"Where does he live?" I asked.

"Somewhere over on Oxenthorpe Road, t'other side of the town. Go and see him. He's a great man."

So I thanked the mussel-man, took up my squirrel again, and started off towards the Oxenthorpe Road.

The first thing I heard as I came into the market place was some one calling, "Meat! M-E-A-T!"

"There's Matthew Mugg," I said to myself. "He'll know where this Doctor lives. Matthew knows everyone."

So I hurried across the market place and caught him up. Off we went together.

"I've known John Dolittle for years and years," said Matthew as we made our way out of the market place. "But I'm pretty sure he ain't home just now. He's away on a voyage. But he's liable to be back any day. I'll show you his house and then you'll know where to find him."

All the way down the Oxenthorpe Road Matthew hardly stopped talking about his great friend, Doctor John Dolittle—"M.D."

150

"Where did the Doctor go on this voyage?" I asked.

"I couldn't tell you," he answered. "Nobody never knows where he goes, nor when he's going, nor when he's coming back. He lives all alone except for his pets."

We were now come beyond the edge of the town. And the house that Matthew pointed out was quite a small one standing by itself. There seemed to be a big garden around it; and this garden was much higher than the road, so you had to go up a flight of steps in the wall before you reached the front gate at the top. I could see that there were many fine fruit trees in the garden, for their branches hung down over the wall in places.

When we reached the house, Matthew went up the steps to the front gate and I followed him. I thought he was going to go into the garden; but the gate was locked. A dog came running down from the house and he took several pieces of meat which the cat's-meat-man pushed through the bars of the gate, and some paper bags full of corn and bran. I noticed that this dog did not stop to eat the meat, but took all the things back to the house and disappeared.

"The Doctor isn't back yet," said Matthew, "or the gate wouldn't be locked."

"What were all those things in paper bags you gave the dog?" I asked.

"Oh, those were provisions," said Matthew, "things for the animals to eat. The Doctor's house is simply full of pets. I give the things to the dog, Jip, while the Doctor's away, and Jip gives them to the other animals."

One Monday afternoon towards the end of April my father asked me to take some shoes which he had mended to a house on the other side of the town. I left the shoes off and then I thought that before I went home I would go and see if the Doctor had come back yet. I had been to his house once already that morning. But I thought I'd just like to go and take another look. My squirrel wasn't getting any better, and I was beginning to be worried about him.

So I turned into the Oxenthorpe Road and started off towards the Doctor's house. On the way I noticed that the sky was clouding over and that it looked as though it might rain.

I reached the gate and found it locked. The dog, Jip, came to the gate and wagged his tail as usual, and then sat down and watched me closely to see that I didn't get in.

I turned away sadly, went down the steps on to the road, and turned towards home again. And then all of a sudden the rain came down in torrents. I have never seen it rain so hard. It got dark, almost like night. The wind began to blow; the thunder rolled; the lightning flashed. There was no place handy to take shelter, so I put my head down against the driving wind and started to run towards home.

I hadn't gone very far when my head bumped into something soft and I sat down suddenly on the pavement. I looked up to see whom I had run into. And there in front of me, sitting on the wet pavement like myself, was a little round man with a very kind face. He wore a shabby high hat and in his hand he had a small black bag.

To my great surprise, instead of being angry, the little man began to laugh.

"It was just as much my fault as it was yours," the little man said. "I had my head down too. But look here, we mustn't sit talking like this. You must be soaked. I know I am. How far have you got to go?"

"My home is on the other side of the town," I said, as we picked ourselves up.

"Then come along to my house and get dried. A storm like this can't last."

We started running back down the road together. Presently we stopped.

"Here we are," he said.

I looked up to see where we were and found myself back at the foot of the steps leading to the little house with the garden! My new friend was already running up the steps and opening the gate with some keys he took from his pocket.

The dog, Jip, came rushing out and started jumping up on him and barking with happiness. The rain was splashing down heavier than ever.

"Are you Doctor Dolittle?" I shouted as we sped up the short garden path to the house.

"Yes, I'm Doctor Dolittle," said he, opening the front door. "Get in! Don't bother about wiping your feet. Never mind the mud. Take it in with you. Get in out of the rain!"

The storm had made it dark enough outside; but inside the house, with the door closed, it was as black as night. Then began the most extraordinary noise that I have ever heard. It sounded like all sorts and kinds of animals and birds calling and squeaking and screeching at the same time. The whole front hall seemed to be filling up with animals. I was beginning to get a bit scared when I felt the Doctor take hold of my arm and shout into my ear.

"Don't be frightened. These are just some of my pets." Then he asked, "Have you any matches; mine are all wet?"

"No, I'm afraid I haven't," I called back.

Then the Doctor made some funny clicking noises with his tongue, and I heard someone trundle up the stairs again and start moving about in the rooms above. A moment later I saw the first glimmerings of a light around the landing above. At once all the animals kept quiet.

"I thought you lived alone," I said to the Doctor.

"So I do," said he. "It is Dab-Dab who is bringing the light."

I looked up the stairs trying to make out who was coming. I could not see around the landing, but I heard the most curious sound.

When at last I could look around me, I found that the hall was indeed simply full of animals. It seemed to me that almost every kind of creature from the countryside must be there.

The Doctor took the candlestick from the duck and turned to me.

"Look here," he said. "You must get those wet clothes off. By the way, what is your name?"

"Tommy Stubbins," I said.

"Oh, are you the son of Jacob Stubbins, the shoemaker?"

"Yes," I said.

"Excellent bootmaker, your father," said the Doctor. "Your father made me these boots four years ago," he said, holding up a foot. "Well, now, look here, Stubbins. You've got to change those wet things—and quick."

More candles had been lighted round different parts of the house. We changed our clothes and started a fire in the big chimney.

"Now let's cook some supper," said the Doctor.

After an excellent supper of sausage and bread, I said to the Doctor, "Can you talk in squirrel language?"

"Oh yes. That's an easy language," he said.

So I told him about my sick squirrel and asked if I could bring it to him tomorrow.

"Well, if its leg is badly broken, I think I had better see it tonight. I'll come home with you and take a look at it."

Hugh Lofting

That visit proved to be just the beginning of Tommy's adventures with Doctor Dolittle. And because of this good man, Tommy's dearest wish came true.

*Doctor Dolittle persuaded Tommy's parents to let him go with him on his next voyage. You can read of his adventures in the book from which this story was taken—*The Voyages of Doctor Dolittle, *by Hugh Lofting.*

Thinking About the Story

It was important for Tommy to meet Doctor John Dolittle. How did he happen to find out about the Doctor? What were Tommy's reasons for wanting to meet Doctor Dolittle?

Tommy and the Doctor finally met under rather unusual circumstances. Be prepared to read aloud the part that tells of this meeting.

Tommy's first experience inside Doctor Dolittle's house almost frightened him. Explain why.

List some of the animal noises which Tommy might have heard in Doctor Dolittle's home. What animals might he have seen?

Write an imaginary conversation between Doctor Dolittle and Jip when Doctor Dolittle returned from his trip. What things would they have to tell each other? What questions might they have asked?

Reading Between the Lines

The story doesn't actually say that Dab-Dab understood what Doctor Dolittle said to him, but you know that he did. How do you know?

You do not find anything in the story that says Jip was a dependable watchdog. Yet you know that he was. How do you know?

Nothing in the story says that Doctor Dolittle did not waste any time if he knew an animal needed help. What makes you think this is true?

Nowhere does the story say that Doctor Dolittle was a kind, happy, easy-going person, but you believe he was. Skim the story to find evidence to prove this is true.

Winter Days

THE WEATHER grew colder. Silver Lake was frozen. Snow fell, but always the wind blew the ice clean, drifting the snow into the tall grass of the sloughs and driving it into waves on the low shores.

On the whole white prairie nothing moved but blowing snow, and the only sound in the vast silence was the sound of the wind.

In the snug house Laura and Carrie helped Ma with the housework, and Grace played, running about the big room with toddling short steps. Whenever she was tired of play, she climbed into Mary's lap, for that was the warmest place and Mary would always tell her a story. Listening to stories, Grace would fall asleep. Then Ma laid her in her trundle bed by the stove, and they all settled down for a cozy afternoon of knitting and sewing and crocheting.

Pa did the chores and walked the trap line he had set along the edge of Big Slough. In the lean-to he skinned foxes and coyotes and muskrats, and stretched the furs on boards to dry.

The prairie was so desolate and the wind so cold that Mary did not go out at all. She loved to sit sewing in the pleasant, warm house, taking tiny even stitches with the needle that Laura threaded for her.

At twilight Mary did not put away her sewing. She told Laura, "I can sew when you can't see to, because I see with my fingers."

"You sew more beautifully than I can, anytime," Laura told her. "You always could."

Even Laura liked the cozy afternoons of rocking and stitching and talking a little, though she never would truly enjoy sewing as Mary did. Often she was restless in the house. Then she would walk from window to window, looking into a whirl of snowflakes and listening to the wind, till Ma said gently, "I declare I don't know what gets into you, Laura."

When the sun shone, no matter how cold it was, Laura must go out. When Ma would let them go, she and Carrie, well wrapped up in coats and hoods, with shoes and mittens and mufflers on, went sliding on Silver Lake. Holding hands, they ran a little way and then slid on the dark smooth ice. First on one foot, then on the other, with little runs between slides, they went back and forth, breathless and warm and laughing.

Those were glorious days when they were out in the glitter of the sharp cold. Then it was good to come into the warm close house, and good to eat supper, and through the evening of music and singing and dancing, Laura was the merriest of all.

One stormy day Pa brought a wide square board in by the stove, and with his pencil he marked it off in small squares inside a plain border.

"Whatever are you making, Pa?" Laura asked, and he answered, "Wait and see."

He heated the tip of the poker red-hot in the stove, and carefully he burned black every alternate little square.

"Curiosity killed a cat, Pa," Laura said.

"You look pretty healthy," said Pa. Tantalizing, he sat there whittling until he had made twenty-four small squares of wood. Half of them he laid on the hot stove, turning them until they were burned black all over.

Then he ranged all these pieces in the squares on the board, and set the board on his knees.

"Now, Laura!" he said.

"Now what?" asked Laura.

"These are checkers, and this is a checkerboard. Pull up your chair, and I'll show you how to play checkers."

She learned so well that before the storm ended she had beaten Pa in one game. But after that, they did not play so immoderately. Ma did not care to play, nor Carrie, so after one game Pa always put the board away.

"Checkers is a selfish game," he said, "for only two can play it. Bring me the fiddle, Flutterbudget."

There came a night when moonlight shone silver clear. The earth was endless white and the wind was still.

Beyond every window the white world stretched far away in frosty glitter, and the sky was a curve of light. Laura could not settle down to anything. She didn't want to play games. She hardly heard even the music of Pa's fiddle. She did not want to dance, but she felt that she must move swiftly. She must be going somewhere.

Suddenly she exclaimed, "Carrie! Let's go slide on the ice!"

"In the night, Laura?" Ma was astonished.

"It's light outdoors," Laura replied. "Almost as light as day."

"It will be all right, Caroline," Pa said. "There's nothing to hurt them, if they don't stay too long and freeze."

So Ma told them, "You may go for a quick run. Don't stay until you get too cold."

Laura and Carrie hurried into their coats and hoods and mittens. Their shoes were new and the soles thick. Ma had knit their stockings of woolen yarn, and their red flannel underclothes came down over their knees and buttoned in a snug band around each stocking. Their flannel petticoats were thick and warm, and their dresses and their coats were wool, and so were their hoods and mufflers.

Out of the warm house they burst into the breath-taking air that tingled with cold. They ran a race on the snowy path down the low hill to the stables. Then they followed the path that the horses and the cow had made when Pa led them through the snow to water at the hole he had cut in the lake ice.

"We mustn't go near the water hole," Laura said, and she led Carrie along the lake shore until they were well away from it. Then they stopped and looked at the night.

It was so beautiful that they hardly breathed. The great round moon hung in the sky and its radiance poured over a silvery world. Far, far away in every direction stretched motionless flatness, softly shining as if it were made of soft light. In the midst lay the dark smooth lake, and a glittering moonpath stretched across it. Tall grass stood up in black lines from the snow drifted in the sloughs.

The stable lay low and dark near the shore, and on the low hill stood the dark, small surveyors' house, with the yellow light in the window twinkling from its darkness.

"How still it is," Carrie whispered. "Listen how still it is."

Laura's heart swelled. She felt herself a part of the wide land, of the far deep sky and the brilliant moonlight. She wanted to fly. But Carrie was little and almost afraid, so she took hold of Carrie's hand and said, "Let's slide. Come on, run!"

With hands clasped, they ran a little way. Then with right foot first they slid on the smooth ice much farther than they had run.

"On the moonpath, Carrie! Let's follow the moonpath," Laura cried.

And so they ran and slid, and ran and slid again, on the glittering moonpath into the light from the silver moon. Farther and farther from shore they went, straight toward the high bank on the other side.

They swooped and almost seemed to fly. If Carrie lost her balance, Laura held her up. If Laura was unsteady, Carrie's hand steadied her.

Close to the farther shore, almost in the shadow of the high bank, they stopped. Something made Laura look up to the top of the bank.

And there, dark against the moonlight, stood a great wolf!

He was looking toward her. The wind stirred his fur and the moonlight seemed to run in and out of it.

"Let's go back," Laura said quickly, as she turned, taking Carrie with her. "I can go faster than you."

She ran and slid and ran again as fast as she could, but Carrie kept up.

"I saw it too," Carrie panted. "Was it a wolf?"

"Don't talk!" Laura answered. "Hurry!"

Laura could hear their feet running and sliding on the ice. She listened for a sound behind them, but there was none. Then they ran and slid without a word until they came to the path by the water hole. As they ran up the path, Laura looked back but she could see nothing on the lake nor on the bank beyond.

Laura and Carrie didn't stop running. They ran up the hill to the house, opened the back door, and ran into the lean-to. They ran across that, burst through the door into the front room and slammed it shut behind them. Then leaned against it, panting.

Pa sprang to his feet. "What is it?" he asked. "What has frightened you?"

"Was it a wolf, Laura?" Carrie gasped.

"It was a wolf, Pa," Laura gulped, catching her breath. "A great big wolf! And I was afraid Carrie couldn't run fast enough, but she did."

"I should say she did!" Pa exclaimed. "Where is this wolf?"

"I don't know. It is gone," Laura told him.

Ma helped them take off their wraps. "Sit down and rest! You are all out of breath," she said.

"Where was the wolf?" Pa wanted to know.

"Up on the bank," Carrie said, and Laura added, "The high bank across the lake."

"Did you girls go clear there?" Pa asked in surprise. "And ran all the way back after you saw him! I had no idea you would go so far. It is a good half-mile."

"We followed the moonpath," Laura told him. Pa looked at her strangely. "You would!" he cried. "I thought those wolves had gone. It was careless of me. I'll hunt them tomorrow."

Mary sat still, but her face was white. "Oh, girls," she almost whispered. "Suppose he had caught you!"

Then they all sat silent while Laura and Carrie rested.

Laura was glad to be safe in the warm room with the desolate prairie shut out. If anything had happened to Carrie, it would have been her fault for taking her so far across the lake.

But nothing had happened. She could almost see again the great wolf with the wind ruffling the moonlight on his fur.

"Pa!" she said in a low voice.

"Yes, Laura?" Pa answered.

"I hope you don't find the wolf, Pa," Laura said.

"Why ever not?" Ma wondered.

"Because he didn't chase us," Laura told her.

"He didn't chase us, Pa, and he could have caught us."

A long wild wolf howl rose and faded away on the stillness. Another answered it. Then silence again.

Laura's heart seemed to turn over with a sickening flop, and she found herself on her feet. She was glad of Ma's steadying hand on her arm.

"Poor girl! You are nervous as a witch and no wonder," Ma said softly.

Ma took a hot flatiron from the back of the stove, wrapped it tightly in a cloth, and gave it to Carrie.

"It is bedtime," she said. "Here is the hot iron for your feet."

"And here is yours, Laura," as she wrapped another. "Be sure you put it in the middle of the bed so Mary's feet can reach it too."

Laura Ingalls Wilder

Finding Word Pictures

Throughout the story there are many words and phrases which help to create a picture of the prairie in winter. These words and phrases not only tell you what it looked like but how it felt to be there. List some of them and be prepared to read them to the group.

The author paints a word picture of the scene which was so beautiful that Laura and Carrie hardly breathed as they looked at it. Be ready to read this part aloud. What feelings did Laura have as she looked at the scene?

Describe the picture that you see in your mind when you read the word "moonpath."

A vivid word picture of the wolf is given in just one sentence. Find this sentence. Tell what you see in your imagination as you read it.

Taking Another Look

What can you learn from the story about family life on the prairie in the late 1800's? What kinds of work did the family do during the winter? How did they spend their leisure time? What was their home like? How did they dress?

Tell how each of the following things was used during pioneer times: lean-to; poker; flatiron; trundle bed.

Pa called Laura a Flutterbudget. Why was this such a good nickname? Find sentences to prove your answer.

The oldest daughter, Mary, was blind. What clues in the story tell you this?

The point of highest interest in the story is called the climax. What is the climax of this story?

Laura hoped that her father would not find the wolf. What was the reason for this? What does this tell you about Laura?

Billy Minds the Baby

ONE SATURDAY AFTERNOON Billy stopped by Fats's house and whistled. Fats stuck his head out an upstairs window and hollered, "I can't come out!" and disappeared before Billy could ask why not.

Billy stayed on the sidewalk and thought this over. Fats might have a job he had to do, in which case Billy didn't want to go bursting in and maybe end up helping Fats wash the windows or wax the floors or something. Just then, one of Fats's little brothers came out of the house, eating an apple.

"Hey, Bobby," called Billy, "what's Fats have to stay in for?"

Bobby took an enormous bite of apple and said, "Ee iee uh agy," with his cheeks bulging.

Billy took the apple away from him and held it up over his head. Bobby chewed hard and swallowed. Then he said, "He's minding the baby. You gimme back my apple."

Billy went into the Martins' house and shouted up the stairs, "Hey, Fats, is it all right if I come up?" The only answer was a loud clattering noise, so Billy went upstairs.

Fats was sitting on the floor beside the baby's crib, reading a book. Benny, the baby, was sitting up in the crib, playing with a pile of clothespins, two kitchen spoons, and an egg beater.

"Ga-loop," said Benny, and threw everything onto the floor. Without looking up from his book, Fats picked them up and threw them back into the crib.

"Hey, what's the idea?" asked Billy. "Everybody's over at the lot playing ball, and I stopped by to get you."

"Well, Mom had to go to town, so she told Ellen to take care of Benny till she gets back." Ellen was Fats's big sister. She was in high school, and whenever Billy tried to phone Fats and kept getting the busy signal, he always knew it was Ellen on the phone, giggling and talking stuff that didn't make sense.

"Why isn't she doing it then?" demanded Billy.

"Oh, some kids came by a while ago, and they were going to the movies, so Ellen asked me to mind him."

Benny got one finger stuck in the egg beater and started to howl. Fats got Benny unstuck from the egg beater and took it away from him. Then Benny yelled louder than ever, so Fats gave it back to him. "I don't mind," he said. "It won't be for long, and besides, she's going to give me fifty cents."

"Fifty cents!" said Billy. "Say, look, I was going over and play ball, but I'll stay and help you mind Benny, if you like."

"No, thanks," said Fats, and picked up his book again.

"Look, why don't you give him his own toys to play with?" Billy pointed to a pile of teddy bears and stuffed animals in the corner.

"He doesn't like 'em. They don't make enough noise when he throws 'em on the floor."

"Then why don't you give him something that'll make a real noise, like some frying pans or something?"

"Look, who's minding this baby, you or me?"

"You are. Catch me hanging around any old baby when I could be out playing ball." Billy went over to the door. "Oh, I almost forgot. Stew Wilson's got a new catcher's mitt. Brand-new! He says he'd better do the catching from now on, and you can play in the outfield if you like, and maybe it'll run some of the fat off you."

Fats jumped up and dropped the book on the floor. Benny gurgled happily, and threw the egg beater after it. "*Stew Wilson!*" roared Fats. "Catcher's mitt! Stew Wilson couldn't catch a ball with a clothes basket. I'll fix him!"

Benny threw the clothespins and the spoons after the egg beater, and began to holler. Fats tossed them back. "Now, look," he said, "you were so anxious to mind Benny. Go ahead and mind him for a while. I won't be long."

Billy gulped. It was one thing to help Fats mind Benny. Being left all alone with Benny was something else again. It was all right for Fats; Fats was used to babies. Billy looked at Benny. Benny was chewing on a clothespin and sort of growling over it, and his teeth looked awfully sharp.

"Why don't we just take him along with us?" asked Billy.

"O. K. if you can find the stroller. Last I saw of it, Bobby and some kids were coasting down Elm Street in it. You get it while I get Benny's sweater and shoes on."

Billy hurried out, for fear Fats would decide to look for the stroller and leave him to get Benny's clothes on. He found it in somebody's front hedge a block away, and when he got back, Fats had Benny all ready. He stuffed him in the stroller, and dumped his old catcher's mitt in on top of him. Benny picked it right up and started chewing on it.

When they got to the vacant lot, the game was still going on. It was a pretty good game, with enough fellows for two whole teams if they played with only two outfielders. The team that Billy and Fats usually played on was in the field, with Gus Schultz pitching and Stew Wilson catching.

Fats parked the stroller near home plate, and just stood there and stared at Stew. Stew pretended not to notice him, but he began to act sort of nervous. Pretty soon he let the ball get away from him, and it rolled a long way into some bushes at the edge of the field.

While Stew was chasing the ball, Fats pried his mitt away from Benny, and picked up a spare ball and tossed it to Gus. Then he pounded his fist in the mitt and hollered, "All right, Gus, put 'er there!"

By the time Stew got back with the lost ball, the game was going right on without him, and Fats was catching. Stew let out a few squawks, but nobody paid any attention to him, so he threw his mitt on the ground and sat down and sulked.

Billy could have got into the game, but he was worried about Benny. When Fats took the mitt away from him, Benny started to yell, and by now he had yelled himself purple in the

face. Billy was afraid that if he yelled any harder, he would hurt something, and then he and Fats would be in trouble, for sure.

Nobody was watching, so he joggled the stroller back and forth a little, the way he had noticed people doing with babies, and Benny almost quit yelling. Billy handed him a little toy truck that someone had dropped, and when Benny started to chew on it, Billy relaxed. He parked the stroller over to one side, out of the way, and went back to the ball game.

By that time Gus had retired the other side, and Billy got into the game. The next inning was a lulu. Nearly everybody got a hit, and Fats hit a homer that went all the way across the street and landed in the Hannagans' vegetable garden. The little kids that were always hanging around went tearing after it.

Maybe they did step on some lettuce or something, but nobody could figure out how they could have done as much damage as Mrs. Hannagan said they did when she came over to complain about it. After a while Mrs. Hannagan went home and the game went on.

When Billy came up to bat for the second time, there was one out and the bases were loaded. Before Billy could even get a crack at the ball, Shorty Morton stole second. As there was a man on second already, that made two out and two on. After the argument about this was finally over, Billy took a swing at a good, fast pitch.

He could tell from the crack of the bat that it was a long one, and he started for first at full speed. Everybody was yelling and hollering like mad and he thought they were cheering him on, but by the time he reached home, all the noise had stopped. When he pulled up and looked around, the lot was practically empty.

There was nobody in sight except Fats and Stew Wilson, and they were both hollering at him. "You busted a window at Mrs. Hannagan's," shouted Fats. "Where's Benny?"

Stew was squawking. "Listen, you guys, I put my brand-new catcher's mitt right *here*, and it's gone, and I'm not going home without it. Look here, Fats Martin, you think you're so smart; what did you do with my mitt?"

Billy couldn't take it all in at once. "I left Benny right here," he said, pointing at the empty stroller. "Say, where is he, anyway?"

"How would I know?" asked Fats. "I thought you were watching him. He might be anywhere by now." He lifted up his voice and bellowed, "Benneeeeee!" But there was no answer.

There was no sign of Benny anywhere. "Well, we better find him, and fast," said Billy. "Listen, Stew, shut up about your old mitt. Fats has lost Benny."

"What do you mean, I've lost Benny. You lost him. You had him last."

Mrs. Hannagan was advancing across centerfield, carrying a baseball and wearing a very unpleasant expression.

Billy talked fast. "Never mind. Stew, you look down Raymond Street. We'll help you find your mitt later. Fats, try the back street. I'll go through the fence—"

"No, you won't, young man." A hand fell on Billy's shoulder.

"So, Billy Kidwell. I might have known it," said Mrs. Hannagan. "And the fat Martin boy. And I know you, too, so you needn't try sneaking off. You're one of the Wilsons. This time I think I'll go straight to your parents. This ball came through my window, and such a mess of broken glass—I ought to make you come right over and clean it up."

"We haven't got time, right now," said Fats. "Billy's lost Benny. Anyway, Benny's lost. We left him right here in the stroller and now he's gone. He can't walk yet, but he can crawl like a flash."

"My goodness!" exclaimed Mrs. Hannagan. "I'll help you look for him. What was he wearing?"

"Overalls and a red sweater," said Fats. "And white shoes and socks, but I wouldn't count on it. He takes 'em off every chance he gets."

"All right," said Mrs. Hannagan briskly. "Now you three each take a different direction, and I'll go this way. And hurry, before he crawls out in the street somewhere. Goodness, such carelessness!" She hurried off.

Fats and Stew each dashed off in a different direction, and Billy started too. Then he stopped. Way down at the end of the vacant lot, he saw a little metal truck. He picked it up, and sure enough, it was dented all over with tooth marks. It was near some pretty thick bushes, and Billy got down on his hands and knees and looked into them.

He saw something red in the bushes, which turned out to be Benny's sweater, with Benny in it. Billy crawled into the bushes, and there was Benny, perfectly happy, chewing on Stew Wilson's brand-new catcher's mitt. Only by now the edges had a funny, scraped look, and the thumb was all wet and dented from Benny's teeth.

Benny's sweater was snagged on some branches, and Billy had quite a time dragging him out, but as long as Benny could go on chewing the mitt, he didn't seem to mind. Billy stuffed him into the stroller, mitt and all, and looked around for Fats and Stew.

He caught up with Fats, two streets over, still yelling, "Benneee!" and together they went and found Stew.

"Look, we found your mitt!" shouted Billy. "Benny had it all the time."

Stew let out a yell when he saw what Benny had done to his nice new mitt, and Benny let out a yell when Stew grabbed it away from him. But Fats handed him the old mitt, quick, and he shut up.

"Aw, a shiny new mitt always looks like a kid's toy," Fats said to Stew. "Now you take one that's all scratched and limbered up, why, it looks like the real thing. Say, how's about

coming over some evening, and we'll take turns pitching to each other. Just for practice, huh?"

"Say that would be swell," said Stew. "Thanks. Well, see you later."

While they were pushing Benny home, Billy said suddenly, "Say, we forgot all about Mrs. Hannagan."

"I guess she's given up by now and gone home," said Fats.

Mrs. Martin was home by the time they got there. "Oh, there you are," she exclaimed. "I was just beginning to get worried. Where's Ellen?"

"Isn't she back yet?" asked Fats. "She went to the movies."

"Oh, she did, did she?" said Fats's mother. "I'll have to see about that. She turned down a sitting job for pay to stay home with Benny, so I offered her a dollar for it. I think perhaps I'll just give you the dollar, instead, since you did the work for her. Perhaps that will teach Ellen to take her responsibilities more seriously."

And she did. She gave Fats a whole dollar. "Divide with Billy, if he's been helping you," she said, and carried Benny upstairs.

Billy said gloomily, "Well, I know what I'll have to do with my share."

"You mean Hannagans' window?"

Billy nodded.

"Why don't you go now, and get it over with?" asked Fats. "Then Mrs. Hannagan won't tell your mother. I'll go with you."

When they got to the Hannagans', Billy was glad to see it was a little pane of glass. The big ones cost more. Mrs. Hannagan answered the door, looking hot and flustered, and they could hear a baby crying somewhere in the house.

178

"Well, it's about time you showed up!" she exclaimed. "By the time I found that baby, you were all gone, and he's been crying ever since. I was just about to phone your mother to come and get him."

Billy looked at Fats. Fats looked at Billy.

"Uh—could we see him, please?" asked Fats cautiously.

"See him? Of course you can see him! You can take him with you!"

She went and got the baby. It was a baby about the same general size as Benny, and it was wearing a red sweater, and it was hollering its head off. She handed it to Fats. Fats joggled it expertly until it almost quit crying.

As soon as Billy could make himself heard, he said, "Mrs. Hannagan, I was the one that busted the window, and I came to see about paying for it."

"Why, that's very honest of you," she said. She seemed to feel a whole lot more cheerful, now that she had the baby off her hands. "Those small panes aren't really so very expensive. I think fifty cents would probably do."

Billy paid her out of the dollar.

"And as for *you*," she said severely to Fats, "I certainly hope this will be a lesson to you to take better care of that poor little thing in the future."

"Yes, ma'am," said Fats. "Uh—where did you say you found him?"

"Mercy, he was clear up in the next block. You know that white house with the big tree in the side yard? Well, he was playing in that yard. Heaven only knows how he crawled that far, and across a street, too."

"Yes, ma'am," said Fats. "Well, thanks a lot."

As soon as the door closed behind Mrs. Hannagan, they started up the street toward the white house with the big tree, Fats lugging the baby Mrs. Hannagan had found.

"Boy, I only hope they haven't missed him yet," said Billy.

"Oh, it won't matter," said Fats. "We'll just say he was way down the street, and we thought we'd better bring him home. And that's the truth too," he added.

Marion Holland

Thinking About the Story

Fats was reading a book and minding his brother Benny. He probably was not planning to play baseball that afternoon. What events made Fats decide to go to the baseball lot and to take Benny along?

Why did such an interesting, exciting game end so abruptly?

Which person do you think was actually responsible for Benny's getting lost?

The boys didn't tell Mrs. Hannagan that the baby she found was not Benny. Why do you think they quietly took the baby home? What would you have done under these circumstances? Why?

There are many humorous incidents in this story. Tell about the one which you enjoyed the most.

Have you ever had the experience of taking care of a baby or a younger child? Be ready to tell the group about your experience. Make a list of things to remember when you accept such a responsibility.

Discussing the Story Characters

Billy becomes involved in some rather unusual situations. Give examples from the story to show how he managed to meet them. Do you think you would like to have Billy as a friend? Why or why not?

Fats and Stew are two very different boys. Tell how they are different. What is your opinion of the way Fats managed to get into the game and take Stew's place? Why do you think Fats promised to play catch with Stew? Why did this make Stew so happy?

Tell how you think Ellen might have felt when she heard what happened while she was gone.

The Wonderful Adventure
of Nils

IT WOULD BE HARD to imagine a more wonderful adventure than the one which befell Nils one spring morning when he was fourteen years old. He started flying across Sweden!

"But what is so remarkable about that?" you may ask. "People fly across Sweden every day."

It is quite true that they do, but not as Nils did. Nils went flying off on the back of a white goose! It happened this way.

Nils had been very bad that Sunday morning. But then, Nils was bad most of the time. It would be hard to find anything good to say about that boy. He threw his wooden shoes at the cows; he tore up birds' nests wherever he could find them; and on this particular Sunday he refused to go with his father and mother to church.

Then it was that the barn elf appeared upon the scene.
Hardly had Nils's parents departed than the elf appeared to
Nils. The next thing Nils knew, he was no bigger than an
elf, himself. There he was in his leather coat and breeches,
with tiny wooden shoes upon his feet, and only a finger's length
long.

When Nils went to plead with the elf to restore him to his
full sturdy height, he saw a flight of wild geese circling above
the barnyard, calling to the tame geese to join them in flight.
To his horror, Nils saw their own white gander flap his wings
and try to fly. Forgetting how he had changed, Nils took
one leap right down into the goose flock and threw his arms
around the neck of the gander.

"Oh, no! You don't fly away this time, sir!" he cried.

The next thing Nils knew, the gander was rising into the air
with Nils clinging to him. There was nothing for the boy
to do but climb aboard the white gander's back and settle
himself between his wings.

The leader of the wild geese was named Akka, and she was wise. For the first two days that they traveled together, she would not tell Nils whether or not he was to be allowed to stay with the flight. They were on their way to Lapland, and Nils knew he wanted very much to go with them. Flying on swift wings above the farms and castles of Sweden was much more fun than staying home and doing the chores.

On the third morning the geese were awake at daybreak. Now the boy felt sure that he'd have to go home; but, curiously enough, both he and the white gander were permitted to follow the wild ones on their morning tour. The boy couldn't understand the reason for the delay, but was glad for every moment that should pass before he must face his parents.

The wild geese traveled to a wide field to eat grass roots, and they kept this up for hours. In the meantime, the boy wandered in the great park which bordered the field. He hunted up a beechnut grove and began to look up at the bushes, to see if a nut from last fall still hung there. Again and again the thought of the trip came over him as he walked in the park. He pictured to himself what a fine time he would have if he went with the wild geese. To freeze and starve: that he believed he should have to do often enough, but in return he would escape both work and study.

When the wild geese had finally eaten themselves full, they bore off toward the lake again, where they amused themselves with games until almost dinnertime.

When they tired of play, they flew out on the ice and rested for a couple of hours. The afternoon they spent in pretty much the same way as the forenoon. First, a couple of hours feeding, then bathing and play in the water near the ice-edge until sunset, when they immediately arranged themselves for sleep.

"This is just the life that suits me," thought the boy when he crept in under the gander's wing. "But tomorrow I suppose I'll be sent home."

Before he fell asleep, he lay and thought that if he might go along with the wild geese, he would escape all scoldings because he was lazy. Then he could cut loose every day, and his only worry would be to get something to eat. But he needed so little nowadays, and there would always be a way to get that.

So he pictured the whole scene to himself; what he should see, and all the adventures that he would share. Yes, it would be something different from the wear and tear at home.

"If only I could go with the wild geese on their travels, I shouldn't grieve because I'd been transformed," thought the boy.

He wasn't afraid of anything—except being sent home; but not even on Wednesday did the geese say anything to him about going. That day passed in the same way as Tuesday, and the boy grew more and more contented with the outdoor life. He thought that he had the lovely Ovid Cloister park—which was as large as a forest—all to himself, and he wasn't anxious to go back to the stuffy cabin and the little patch of ground there at home.

On Wednesday he believed that the wild geese thought of keeping him with them, but on Thursday he lost hope again.

Thursday began just like the other days; the geese fed on the broad meadows, and the boy hunted for food in the park. After a while Akka came to him and asked if he had found anything to eat. No, he had not; and then she searched for a dry caraway herb that still had all its tiny seeds.

When the boy had eaten, Akka said that she thought he ran around in the park altogether too recklessly. She wondered if he realized how many enemies he had to guard against—he, who was so little. No, he didn't know anything at all about that. Then Akka began to enumerate them for him.

Whenever he walked in the park, she said he must look out for the fox and the marten. When he came to the shores of the lake, he must think of the otters. As he sat on the stone wall, he must not forget the weasels, who could creep through the smallest holes. And if he wished to lie down and sleep on a pile of leaves, he must first find out if the adders were not sleeping their winter sleep in the same pile.

As soon as he came out in the open field, he should keep an eye out for hawks and buzzards, for eagles and falcons that soared in the air. In the bramble bush he could be captured by the sparrow hawks. Magpies and crows were found everywhere and in these he mustn't place too much confidence. As soon as it was dusk, he must keep his ears open and listen for the big owls, who flew along with such soundless wing strokes that they could come right up to him before he was aware of them.

When the boy heard that there were so many who were after his life, he thought that it would be simply impossible for him to escape. He was not particularly afraid to die. But he didn't like the idea of being eaten up, so he asked Akka what he should do to protect himself from these animals.

186

Akka answered at once that the boy should try to get on good terms with all the small animals in the woods and fields: with the squirrel-folk and the hare-family; with bullfinches and titmice and woodpeckers and larks. If he made friends with them, they could warn him against dangers, find hiding places for him, and protect him.

But later in the day, when the boy tried to profit by this advice, and turned to Sirle Squirrel to ask for his protection, it was evident that he did not care to help him.

"You surely can't expect anything from me, or the rest of the small animals!" said Sirle. "Don't you think we know that you are Nils the goose boy, who tore down the swallow's nest last year, crushed the starling's eggs, threw baby crows in the marl ditch, caught thrushes in snares, and put squirrels in cages? You just help yourself as well as you can. You may be thankful that we do not form a league against you and drive you back to your own kind!"

This was just the sort of answer the boy would not have let go unpunished in the days when he was Nils the goose boy. But now he was only fearful lest the wild geese, too, had found out how wicked he could be. He had been so anxious for fear he wouldn't be permitted to stay with the wild geese, that he hadn't dared to get into the least little mischief since he joined their company.

All day Thursday he thought it was surely on account of his wickedness that the wild geese did not care to take him along up to Lapland. And in the evening, when he heard that Sirle Squirrel's wife had been stolen, and her children were starving to death, he made up his mind to help them.

At great risk to himself he went into every farmhouse roundabout until he found the one where the mother squirrel

was held captive. But he couldn't free her, for the lock on the door of her cage was too heavy for him. He found out from her where her babies were, and climbed the tree and brought them to her cage, one by one. In the morning the farm folk were so touched at sight of the baby squirrels restored to their mother, that they took the whole squirrel family out to the hazel grove and let them have their freedom again.

When the boy came into the park on Friday, he heard the bullfinches sing in every bush of how Sirle Squirrel's wife had been carried away from her children by cruel robbers. They told how Nils the goose boy had risked his life among human beings, and had taken the little squirrel children to her.

"And who is so honored in Ovid Cloister park now, as Thumbietot," sang the bullfinch, "he, whom all feared when he was Nils the goose boy? Sirle Squirrel will give him nuts. The poor hares are going to play with him. The small wild animals will carry him on their backs and fly away with him when Smirre Fox approaches."

The boy was certain that both Akka and the wild geese had heard all this. But still Friday passed, and not one word did they say about his remaining with them.

Then Sunday came again. A whole week had gone by since the boy had been bewitched.

Nils was down by the lake that afternoon, playing on a reed pipe when he saw the geese coming toward him. They walked so uncommonly slow and dignified-like that he immediately understood that now he should learn what they intended to do with him.

"We are grateful for the help you have given us," Akka said to him. "I have sent word to the elf that bewitched you. I have told him how well you have conducted yourself among us. He greets you and says that as soon as you turn back home, you shall be human again."

But think of it! Just as happy as the boy had been when the wild geese began to speak, just that miserable was he when they had finished. He didn't say a word, but turned away and wept.

"What in all the world is this?" said Akka. "It looks as though you had expected more of me than I have offered you."

But the boy was thinking of the carefree days and the banter, of the adventure and freedom and travel, high above the earth, that he should miss, and he actually bawled with grief.

"I don't want to be human," said he. "I want to go with you to Lapland."

"I'll tell you something," said Akka. "That elf is very touchy, and I'm afraid that if you do not accept his offer now, it will be difficult for you to coax him another time."

It was a strange thing about that boy—as long as he had lived, he had never cared for anyone. He had not cared for his teacher, nor for his schoolmates, nor for the boys in the neighborhood. All that they had wished to have him do—whether it had been work or play—he had only thought tiresome. Therefore there was no one whom he missed or longed for.

"I don't want to be human," bawled the boy. "I want to go with you to Lapland. That's why I've been good for a whole week!"

"I don't want to forbid you to come along with us as far as you like," said Akka, "but think first if you wouldn't rather go home again. A day may come when you will regret this."

"No," said the boy, "that's nothing to regret. I have never been so well off as here with you."

"Well, then, let it be as you wish," said Akka.

"Thanks," said the boy, and he felt so happy that he had to cry for very joy—just as he had cried before from sorrow.

So Nils traveled all that summer with the wild geese and had many wonderful adventures. He saw the whole land of Sweden and he learned many things about himself as he faced danger and hardship with his winged friends. By the time autumn had come again, he was ready to become a human being once more. During the course of his travels he had learned the value of humankind.

Selma Lagerlöf

The whole story of Nils is told in a book by Selma Lagerlöf, the great Swedish author who won the Nobel Prize for literature. It is called The Wonderful Adventures of Nils.

Thinking About the Story

Something very strange happened to Nils after his father and mother left for church. What was it? Be ready to tell about it.

Why did Nils enjoy his new life? What was the one thing he was afraid would happen? Why did Nils keep out of mischief for a whole week?

Nils received some advice from Akka. What was it? Why wasn't he able to profit from this advice? How did Nils finally win the respect and the friendship of the small animals?

Nils cried twice in the story but for very different reasons. What were these reasons?

Nils's adventure brought about a great change in him. What kind of a person was he at first? At the end of the story Nils had learned a lesson. What was it? How do you think that facing danger and hardship might have helped him to learn this?

The elf offered once to return Nils to his normal size, but Nils refused. At the end of the story Nils wished to become a human being. Do you think he succeeded? Write your own story of this adventure.

Exploring Beyond the Story

The story refers to Nils as having been transformed and bewitched. Explain the meanings of the words *transformed* and *bewitched*. Use your glossary to help you.

Look for information about Sweden and Lapland in a reference book or encyclopedia. What would you expect to see if you were to travel there? Imagine you are Nils and write a description of what you saw as you went flying over this country with the wild geese.

A Mad Tea-Party

THERE WAS A TABLE set out under a tree in front of the house, and the March Hare and the Hatter were having tea at it. A Dormouse was sitting between them, fast asleep, and the other two were using it as a cushion, resting their elbows on it, and talking over its head. "Very uncomfortable for the Dormouse," thought Alice; "only as it's asleep, I suppose it doesn't mind."

The table was a large one, but the three were all crowded together at one corner of it. "No room! No room!" they cried out when they saw Alice coming.

"There's *plenty* of room!" said Alice indignantly, and she sat down in a large armchair at one end of the table.

"Have some wine," the March Hare said in an encouraging tone.

194

Alice looked all round the table, but there was nothing on it but tea. "I don't see any wine," she remarked.

"There isn't any," said the March Hare.

"Then it wasn't very civil of you to offer it," said Alice angrily.

"It wasn't very civil of you to sit down without being invited," said the March Hare.

"I didn't know it was your table," said Alice. "It's laid out for a great many more than three."

"Your hair wants cutting," said the Hatter. He had been looking at Alice for some time with great curiosity, and this was his first speech.

"You should learn not to make personal remarks," Alice said with some severity. "It's very rude."

The Hatter opened his eyes very wide on hearing this, but all he said was "Why is a raven like a writing desk?"

"Come, we shall have some fun now!" thought Alice. "I'm glad they've begun asking riddles. . . . I believe I can guess that," she added aloud.

"Do you mean that you think you can find out the answer to it?" said the March Hare.

"Exactly so," said Alice.

"Then you should say what you mean," the March Hare went on.

"I do," Alice hastily replied. "At least—at least I mean what I say—that's the same thing, you know."

"Not the same thing a bit!" said the Hatter. "Why, you might just as well say that 'I see what I eat' is the same thing as 'I eat what I see'!"

"You might just as well say," added the March Hare, "that 'I like what I get' is the same thing as 'I get what I like'!"

"You might just as well say," added the Dormouse, which seemed to be talking in its sleep, "that 'I breathe when I sleep' is the same thing as 'I sleep when I breathe'!"

"It *is* the same thing with you," said the Hatter, and here the conversation dropped, and the party sat silent for a minute, while Alice thought over all she could remember about ravens and writing desks, which wasn't much.

The Hatter was the first to break the silence. "What day of the month is it?" he said, turning to Alice. He had taken his watch out of his pocket and was looking at it uneasily, shaking it every now and then, and holding it to his ear.

Alice considered a little, and said, "The fourth."

"Two days wrong!" sighed the Hatter. "I told you butter wouldn't suit the works!" he added, looking angrily at the March Hare.

"It was the best butter," the March Hare meekly replied.

"Yes, but some crumbs must have got in as well," the Hatter grumbled. "You shouldn't have put it in with the bread knife."

The March Hare took the watch and looked at it gloomily. Then he dipped it into his cup of tea, and looked at it again, but he could think of nothing better to say than his first remark, "It was the best butter, you know."

Alice had been looking over his shoulder with some curiosity. "What a funny watch!" she remarked. "It tells the day of the month, and doesn't tell what o'clock it is!"

"Why should it?" muttered the Hatter. "Does your watch tell you what year it is?"

"Of course not," Alice replied very readily, "but that's because it stays the same year for such a long time."

"Which is just the case with mine," said the Hatter.

Alice felt dreadfully puzzled. The Hatter's remark seemed to her to have no sort of meaning in it, and yet it was certainly English. "I don't quite understand you," she said politely.

"The Dormouse is asleep again," said the Hatter, and he poured a little hot tea upon its nose.

The Dormouse shook its head impatiently and said, without opening its eyes, "Of course, of course, just what I was going to remark myself."

"Have you guessed the riddle yet?" the Hatter said, turning to Alice again.

"No, I give it up," Alice replied. "What's the answer?"

"I haven't the slightest idea," said the Hatter.

"Nor I," said the March Hare.

Alice sighed wearily. "I think you might do something better with the time," she said, "than wasting it in asking riddles that have no answers."

"If you knew Time as well as I do," said the Hatter, "you wouldn't talk about wasting *it*. It's *him*."

"I don't know what you mean," said Alice.

"Of course you don't!" the Hatter said, tossing his head contemptuously. "I dare say you never even spoke to Time!"

"Perhaps not," Alice cautiously replied, "but I know I have to beat time when I learn music."

"Ah! That accounts for it," said the Hatter. "He won't stand beating. Now, if you only kept on good terms with him, he'd do almost anything you liked with the clock. For instance, suppose it were nine o'clock in the morning, just time to begin lessons: you'd only have to whisper a hint to Time, and round goes the clock in a twinkling! Half past one, time for dinner!"

"I only wish it was," the March Hare said to himself in a whisper.

"That would be grand, certainly," said Alice thoughtfully, "but then—I shouldn't be hungry for it, you know."

"Not at first, perhaps," said the Hatter, "but you could keep it to half past one as long as you liked."

"Is that the way you manage?" Alice asked.

The Hatter shook his head mournfully. "Not I," he replied. "We quarreled last March—just before he went mad, you know—" (pointing with his teaspoon at the March Hare) "—it was at the great concert given by the Queen of Hearts, and I had to sing:

> '*Twinkle, twinkle, little bat!*
> *How I wonder what you're at!*'

You know the song, perhaps?"

"I've heard something like it," said Alice.

"It goes on, you know," the Hatter continued, "in this way:

> '*Up above the world you fly,*
> *Like a tea tray in the sky.*
> *Twinkle, twinkle . . .*'"

Here the Dormouse shook itself, and began singing in its sleep, "Twinkle, twinkle, twinkle, twinkle . . ." and went on so long that they had to pinch it to make it stop.

"Well, I'd hardly finished the first verse," said the Hatter, "when the Queen bawled out: 'He's murdering the time! Off with his head!'"

"How dreadfully savage!" exclaimed Alice.

"And ever since that," the Hatter went on in a mournful tone, "he won't do a thing I ask! It's always six o'clock now."

A bright idea came into Alice's head. "Is that the reason so many tea things are put out here?" she asked.

"Yes, that's it," said the Hatter with a sigh. "It's always teatime, and we've no time to wash the things between whiles."

"Then you keep moving round, I suppose?" said Alice.

"Exactly so," said the Hatter, "as the things get used up."

"But when you come to the beginning again?" Alice ventured to ask.

"Suppose we change the subject," the March Hare interrupted, yawning. "I'm getting tired of this. I vote the young lady tells us a story."

"I'm afraid I don't know one," said Alice, rather alarmed at the proposal.

"Then the Dormouse shall!" And they pinched it on both sides at once.

The Dormouse slowly opened its eyes. "I wasn't asleep," it said in a hoarse, feeble voice, "I heard every word you fellows were saying."

"Tell us a story!" said the March Hare.

"Yes, please do!" pleaded Alice.

"And be quick about it," added the Hatter, "or you'll be asleep again before it's done."

"Once upon a time there were three little sisters," the Dormouse began in a great hurry; "and their names were Elsie, Lacie, and Tillie; and they lived at the bottom of a well . . ."

"What did they live on?" said Alice, who always took a great interest in questions of eating and drinking.

"They lived on treacle," said the Dormouse, after thinking a minute or two.

"They couldn't have done that, you know," Alice gently remarked. "They'd have been ill."

"So they were," said the Dormouse; "very ill."

Alice tried a little to fancy to herself what such an extraordinary way of living would be like, but it puzzled her too much; so she went on, "But why did they live at the bottom of a well?"

"Take some more tea," the March Hare said to Alice, very earnestly.

"I've had nothing yet," Alice replied in an offended tone, "so I can't take more."

"You mean you can't take less," said the Hatter. "It's very easy to make more than nothing."

"Nobody asked your opinion," said Alice.

"Who's making personal remarks now?" the Hatter asked triumphantly.

Alice did not quite know what to say to this; so she helped herself to some tea and bread and butter, and then turned to the Dormouse, and repeated her question. "Why did they live at the bottom of a well?"

The Dormouse again took a minute or two to think about it, and then said, "It was a treacle well."

"There's no such thing!" Alice was beginning very angrily, but the Hatter and the March Hare went "Sh! Sh!" and the Dormouse sulkily remarked, "If you can't be civil, you'd better finish the story for yourself."

"No, please go on!" Alice said very humbly. "I won't interrupt you again. I dare say there may be one."

"One, indeed!" said the Dormouse indignantly. However, he consented to go on. "And so these three little sisters—they were learning to draw, you know . . ."

"What did they draw?" said Alice, quite forgetting her promise.

"Treacle," said the Dormouse, without considering at all, this time.

"I want a clean cup," interrupted the Hatter. "Let's all move one place on."

He moved on as he spoke, and the Dormouse followed him sleepily. The March Hare moved into the Dormouse's place, and Alice rather unwillingly took the place of the March Hare. The Hatter was the only one who got any real advantage from the change, and Alice was a good deal worse off than before, as the March Hare had just upset the jug of milk into his plate.

Alice did not wish to offend the Dormouse again, so she began very cautiously, "But I don't understand. Where did they draw the treacle from?"

"You can draw water out of a water well," said the Hatter, "so I should think you could draw treacle out of a treacle well, eh, stupid?"

"But they were *in* the well," Alice said to the Dormouse, not choosing to notice this last remark.

"Of course they were," said the Dormouse, "well in."

This answer so confused poor Alice that she let the Dormouse go on for some time without interrupting it.

"They were learning to draw," the Dormouse went on, yawning and rubbing its eyes, for it was getting very sleepy; "and they drew all manner of things—everything that begins with an M . . ."

"Why with an M?" said Alice.

"Why not?" said the March Hare.

Alice was silent.

The Dormouse had closed its eyes by this time, and was going off into a doze, but, on being pinched by the Hatter, it woke up again with a little shriek, and went on: " . . . that begins with an M, such as mousetraps, and the moon, and memory, and muchness—you know you say things are 'much of a muchness'—did you ever see such a thing as a drawing of a muchness!"

"Really, now you ask me," said Alice, very much confused, "I don't think . . ."

"Then you shouldn't talk," said the Hatter.

This piece of rudeness was more than Alice could bear. She got up in great disgust and walked off. The Dormouse fell asleep instantly, and neither the March Hare nor the Hatter took the least notice of her going, though she looked back once or twice, half hoping that they would call after her. The last time she saw them, they were trying to put the Dormouse into the teapot.

"At any rate I'll never go there again!" said Alice, as she picked her way through the wood. "It's the stupidest tea-party I ever was at in all my life!"

Just as she said this, she noticed that one of the trees had a door leading right into it. "That's very curious!" she thought. "But everything's curious today. I think I may as well go in at once." And in she went.

Once more she found herself in the long hall, and close to the little glass table. "Now, I'll manage better this time," she said to herself, and began by taking the little golden key, and unlocking the door that led into the garden. Then she set to work nibbling at the mushroom (she had kept a piece of it in her pocket) till she was about a foot high. Then she walked down the little passage, and then—she found herself at last in the beautiful garden, among the bright flower beds and the cool fountains.

Lewis Carroll

Thinking About the Story

 This story is taken from *Alice in Wonderland*, a book which has long been enjoyed for its delightful humor. One of the things that makes it amusing is the way the characters act. Another is the manner in which they talk. The animals seem to talk nonsense. Find and be ready to read aloud some of the funny things they say.

What do you consider one of the most humorous incidents in the story? Which character do you like the most? Why?

What words would you use to describe how Alice felt at the tea-party?

What did Alice have to do before she could go down the little passage? Where did this lead her? If you could use the little golden key, what kind of place would you wish to have it unlock for you? Write a paragraph describing this place.

Reading the Story Together

Because this story is almost all conversation, it is a good one for the group to read aloud. Decide who will take the parts of the story characters. Choose one person to read the parts which are not conversation.

Try to read as the characters in the story would have talked. Show by the tone of your voice how these characters felt. Read so everyone can hear and understand you.

Planning an Exhibit

Plan an exhibit of the books from which the stories in this unit are taken. There may be copies at the school or the public library. Some children may have copies at home. Other books by these authors, or by other favorite authors, will add to the interest of the exhibit.

Robinson Crusoe's Story

The night was thick and hazy
When the Piccadilly Daisy
Carried down the crew and the captain in the sea;
And I think the water drowned 'em;
For they never, never found 'em,
And I know they didn't come ashore with me.

Oh! 'twas very sad and lonely
When I found myself the only
Population on this cultivated shore;
But I've made a little tavern
In a rocky little cavern,
And I sit and watch for people at the door.

I have a little garden
That I'm cultivating lard in,
As the things I eat are rather tough and dry;
For I live on toasted lizards,
Prickly pears, and parrot gizzards,
And I'm really very fond of beetle pie.

The clothes I had were furry,
And it made me fret and worry
When I found the moths were eating off the hair;
And I had to scrape and sand 'em,
And I boiled 'em and I tanned 'em,
Till I got the fine morocco suit I wear.

I sometimes seek diversion
In a family excursion
With the few domestic animals you see;
And we take along a carrot
As refreshment for the parrot,
And a little can of jungleberry tea.

Then we gather, as we travel,
Bits of moss and dirty gravel,
And we chip off little specimens of stone;
And we carry home as prizes
Funny bugs, of handy sizes,
Just to give the day a scientific tone.

If the roads are wet and muddy,
We remain at home and study,
For the Goat is very clever at a sum,
And the Dog, instead of fighting,
Studies ornamental writing,
While the Cat is taking lessons on the drum.

We retire at eleven,
And we rise again at seven;
And I wish to call attention, as I close,
To ·the fact that all the scholars
Are correct about their collars,
And particular in turning out their toes.

Charles Edward Carryl

Great Stories

209

The Boy Pu-nia and the King of the Sharks

THE NAME of the King of the Sharks was Kai-ale-ale. He lived near a cave that was filled with lobsters. And on account of Kai-ale-ale and the ten sharks he had under him, no one dared to dive down into the cave and take lobsters out of it. The sharks stayed around the cave night and day. If a diver ventured near, they would bite him and devour him.

There was a boy named Pu-nia whose father had been killed by the sharks. Now, after his father had been killed, there was no one to catch fish for Pu-nia and his mother. They had sweet potatoes to eat, but never any fish. Often Pu-nia heard his mother say that she wished she had a fish or lobster to eat with the sweet potatoes. And so the time came when Pu-nia made up his mind that he and his mother would have lobsters to eat.

He stood above the cave where the lobsters were. Looking down, he saw Kai-ale-ale and his ten sharks. They were all asleep. While he was watching them, they wakened. Pu-nia pretended he did not know that they had awakened. He spoke loudly so that they would hear him, and he said, "Here am I, Pu-nia, and I am going into the cave to get lobsters for myself and my mother That great shark, Kai-ale-ale, is asleep now, and I can dive to the point over there, and then go into the cave. I will take two lobsters in my hands, and my mother and I will have something to eat with our sweet potatoes."

Said Kai-ale-ale, speaking softly to the other sharks, "Let us rush to the place where Pu-nia dives, and let us devour him as we devoured his father."

But Pu-nia was a very cunning boy and not at all the sort that could be caught by the stupid sharks. He had a stone in his hand while he was speaking, and he flung it toward the point where he said he was going to dive. Just as soon as the stone struck the water, the sharks made a rush to the place, leaving the cave of the lobsters unguarded. Then Pu-nia dived. He went into the cave, took two lobsters in his hands, and came up out of the water.

And then, from the place where he had spoken before, he shouted down to the sharks, "Here is Pu-nia, and he has come back safely. He has two lobsters, and he and his mother have something to live on. It was the first shark, the second shark, the third shark, the fourth shark, the fifth shark, the sixth shark, the seventh shark, the eighth shark, the ninth shark, the tenth shark—it was the tenth shark, the one with the thin tail, that showed Pu-nia what to do."

When the King of the Sharks, Kai-ale-ale, heard this from Pu-nia, he ordered all the sharks to come together and stay in a row. He counted them, and there were ten of them, and the tenth one had a thin tail. "So it was you, Thin Tail," he said, "that told the boy Pu-nia what to do. You shall die." And then, according to the orders that the King of the Sharks gave, the thin-tailed shark was killed.

Pu-nia called out to them, "You have killed one of your own kind." Then with the two lobsters in his hands, he went back to his mother's.

After the lobsters were eaten, Pu-nia went back to the place above the cave. He called out as he had done the first time, "I can dive to the place over there and then slip into the cave, for Kai-ale-ale and his sharks are all asleep; I can get two lobsters for myself and my mother, so that we'll have something to eat with our sweet potatoes." Then, as before, he threw down a stone and made ready to dive to another point.

When the stone struck the water, the sharks rushed over, leaving the cave unguarded. Then Pu-nia dived down and went into the cave. He took two lobsters in his hands and got back to the top of the water. He shouted down to the sharks from the place where he had stood before, "It was the first shark, the second shark, the third shark, the fourth shark, the fifth shark, the sixth shark, the seventh shark, the eighth shark, the ninth shark—it was the ninth shark, the one with the big stomach, that told Pu-nia what to do."

Then the King of the Sharks, Kai-ale-ale, ordered the sharks to get into a line. He counted them, and he found that the ninth shark had a big stomach. "So it was you who told Pu-nia what to do," he said; and he ordered the big-stomached shark to be killed. After that, Pu-nia went home with his two lobsters, and he and his mother had something to eat with their sweet potatoes.

The boy Pu-nia continued to do this. He would deceive the sharks by throwing a stone to the place where he said he was going to dive. When he got the sharks away from the cave, he would dive down, slip in, and take two lobsters in his hands. And always, when he got to the top of the water, he would name a shark. "The first shark, the second shark, the third shark—the shark with the little eye, the shark with the gray spot on him—told Pu-nia what to do," he would say; and each time he would get one of the sharks killed. Finally, only Kai-ale-ale, the King of the Sharks, was left.

And now Pu-nia wanted to do something against Kai-ale-ale. So he went into the forest and hewed out two hard pieces of wood, each about a yard long, and sticks for kindling a fire. He got charcoal to burn as a fire, and he got food. All these things he put into a bag, and he carried the bag down to the beach. He came above the cave that Kai-ale-ale guarded, and he said, speaking in a loud voice, "If I dive now, and if Kai-ale-ale bites me, my blood will come to the top of the water, and my mother will see the blood and will bring me back to life again. But if I dive down and Kai-ale-ale takes me into his mouth whole, I shall die and never come back to life again."

Kai-ale-ale was listening, of course. He said to himself, "No, I shall not bite you, you cunning boy; I shall take you into my mouth and swallow you whole. I shall open my mouth wide enough to take you in. Yes, this time I shall get you."

Pu-nia dived, holding his bag. Kai-ale-ale opened his mouth wide and got Pu-nia into it. But as soon as the boy got within, he opened his bag and took out the two pieces of wood which he had hewn out in the forest. He put them between the jaws of the shark so that Kai-ale-ale was unable to close them.

Pu-nia, who was inside the big shark, took the fire sticks out of his bag and rubbed them together, making a fire. He kindled the charcoal, and he cooked his food at the fire. With the fire inside of him, the shark could not keep still; he went dashing here and there through the ocean.

At last the shark came near the island of Hawaii. "If he brings me near the breakers, I am saved," said Pu-nia, speaking aloud, "but if he takes me to the sand near where the grass grows, I shall die; I cannot be saved."

Kai-ale-ale, when he heard Pu-nia say this, said to himself, "I will not take him near the breakers. I will take him where the dry sand is, near the grass." Saying this, he dashed in from the ocean and up to a place where the shrubs grew on the shore. No shark had ever gone there before; and when Kai-ale-ale got there, he could not get back again.

Then Pu-nia came out of the shark and shouted, "Kai-ale-ale, Kai-ale-ale, the King of Sharks, has come to visit us." And the people, hearing about their enemy, Kai-ale-ale, came down to the shore with their spears and their knives and killed him. And that was the end of the ugly, wicked King of the Sharks.

Every day after that, Pu-nia was able to go down into the cave and get lobsters for himself and his mother. And the people all rejoiced when they knew that the eleven sharks that guarded the cave had been got rid of by the boy Pu-nia.

Padraic Colum

Thinking About the Story

The story says that Pu-nia was a cunning boy. Why could he be called cunning? What other words would you use to describe Pu-nia?

Why was it necessary for Pu-nia to find some way to outwit the sharks? Tell how he deceived them the first time and what happened as a result.

What did Pu-nia do to deceive Kai-ale-ale after the ten sharks had been killed? How did the two pieces of wood, the charcoal, and the food play an important part in this story? How did Pu-nia deceive the King of the Sharks for the last time? Again the shark showed his stupidity. How?

Retelling a Folk Tale

Folk tales, as you know, are stories that were told and retold by the people of a country from one generation to another. The story you have just read is a very old Hawaiian folk tale.

Pretend that you are a storyteller in Hawaii and plan to tell this folk tale to a group of children who have never heard it. What main ideas will you keep in mind? What important details will you include?

Tell your story so that all can hear and understand you. How can you make it so interesting that your audience will want to remember the story and retell it?

217

Orpheus and Eurydice

Many were the minstrels who, in the early days of the world, went amongst men, telling them stories of the gods, of their births and their wars, and of the beginning of things. Of all these minstrels none was so famous as Orpheus; none could tell truer things about the gods; and there were some who said that he was in truth Apollo's son.

But a great grief came to Orpheus, a grief that stopped his singing and his playing upon the lyre. His young wife, Eurydice, was taken from him. One day, walking in the garden, she was bitten on the heel by a snake; and straightway she went down to the World of the Dead.

Then everything in this world was dark and bitter for the minstrel of the gods. Sleep would not come to him, and for him food had no taste. Then Orpheus said, "I will do that which no mortal has ever done before; I will do that which even the Immortals might shrink from doing; I will go down into the World of the Dead; and I will bring back to the living and to the light my wife, Eurydice."

Then Orpheus went on his way to the cavern which goes down, down to the World of the Dead—the Cavern Tainaron. The trees showed him the way. As he went on, Orpheus played upon his lyre and sang. The trees heard his song and were moved by his grief, and with their arms and their heads they showed him the way to the deep, deep cavern named Tainaron.

Down, down, down by a winding path Orpheus went. He came at last to the great gate that opens upon the World of the Dead. And the silent guards who keep watch there for the Rulers of the Dead were astonished when they saw a living being coming toward them, and they would not let Orpheus approach the gate.

The minstrel took the lyre in his hands and played upon it. As he played, the silent watchers gathered around him, leaving the gate unguarded. As he played, the Rulers of the Dead came forth, Hades and Persephone, and listened to the words of the living man.

"The cause of my coming through the dark and fearful ways," sang Orpheus, "is to strive to gain a fairer fate for Eurydice, my wife. All that is above must come down to you at last, O Rulers of the most lasting World. But before her time has Eurydice been brought here. I have desired strength to endure her loss, but I cannot endure it. And I have come before you, Hades and Persephone, brought here by love."

When Orpheus said the name of love, Persephone, the queen of the dead, bowed her young head, and bearded Hades, the king, bowed his head also. Persephone remembered how Demeter, her mother, had searched for her throughout the world, and she remembered the touch of her mother's tears upon her face. And Hades remembered how his love for Persephone had led him to carry her away from the valley where she had been gathering flowers. He and Persephone stood aside, and Orpheus went through the gate and came amongst the dead.

In amidst the newly-come dead Orpheus saw Eurydice. She
looked upon her husband, but she had not the power to come
near him. But slowly she came when Hades, the king, called
her. Then with joy Orpheus took her hands.

It would be granted them—no mortal ever gained such
privilege before—to leave, both together, the World of the
Dead, and to live for another space in the World of the Living.
One condition there would be—that on their way up neither
Orpheus nor Eurydice should look back.

They went through the gate and came out amongst the
watchers that are around the portals. These showed them the
path that went up to the World of the Living. That way they
went, Orpheus and Eurydice, he going before her.

Up and through the darkened ways they went, Orpheus knowing that Eurydice was behind him, but never looking back upon her. As he went, his heart was filled with things to tell her—how the trees were blossoming in the garden she had left; how the water was sparkling in the fountain; how the doors of the house stood open; how they, sitting together, would watch the sunlight on the laurel bushes. All these things were in his heart to tell her who came behind him, silent and unseen.

And now they were nearing the place where the cavern opened on the World of the Living. Orpheus looked up toward the light from the sky. Out of the opening of the cavern he went; he saw a white-winged bird fly by. He turned around and cried, "O Eurydice, look upon the world I have won you back to!"

He turned to say this to her. He saw her with her long dark hair and pale face. He held out his arms to clasp her. But

in that instant she slipped back into the gloom of the cavern. And all he heard spoken was a single word, "Farewell!" Long, long had it taken Eurydice to climb so far, but in the moment of his turning around, she had fallen back to her place amongst the dead. For Orpheus had looked back.

Back through the cavern Orpheus went again. Again he came before the watchers of the gate. But now he was not looked at nor listened to. Without hope he had to return to the World of the Living.

The birds were his friends now, and the trees and the stones. The birds flew around him and mourned with him. The trees and stones often followed him, moved by the music of his lyre. But a savage band killed Orpheus and threw his head and his lyre into the River Hebrus. It is said by the poets that while they floated in midstream the lyre gave out some mournful notes, and the head of Orpheus answered the notes with song.

Padraic Colum

223

Exploring Beyond the Story

Myths are very old stories which tell about the gods who were supposed to rule the earth. This myth refers to the gods as immortal and to the people as mortal. Discuss what this means. You may want to use your glossary to help you.

Orpheus was a minstrel who was famous for his singing and playing upon the lyre. Learn more about this instrument. Be prepared to tell the class about the lyre.

"Orpheus and Eurydice" is a Greek myth. Look in the encyclopedia or some other reference book and find out from what other countries or parts of the world famous myths have come. Make a list of several myths which your group might read.

Imagining You Were There

Imagine you are Eurydice about to return to the world. How would you feel?

Imagine you are traveling "through the dark and fearful ways." What would you see, feel, hear?

Imagine what would have happened if Orpheus had not turned around. How might the story have ended?

Using Words to Describe

The author speaks of Orpheus as "a living man." We would call him a human being. Look through the story to find the authors way of describing

what the minstrels sang about.

how Orpheus felt after Eurydice's death.

how Orpheus and Eurydice walked along the path.

what Orpheus wanted to show Eurydice once again.

Be ready to read aloud these descriptions.

224

Orpheus with His Lute

Orpheus with his lute made trees,
And the mountaintops that freeze,
   Bow themselves when he did sing.
To his music plants and flowers
Ever sprung, as sun and showers
   There had made a lasting spring.

Everything that heard him play,
Even the billows of the sea,
   Hung their heads, and then lay by.
In sweet music is such art,
Killing care and grief of heart
   Fall asleep, or hearing, die.

William Shakespeare

Beowulf's Fight with Grendel

OLD KING HROTHGAR built for himself a great palace, covered with gold, with benches all round outside, and a terrace leading up to it. It was bigger than any hall men had ever heard of, and there Hrothgar sat on his throne to share with men the good things God had given him. A band of brave knights gathered round him, all living together in peace and joy.

But there came a wicked monster, Grendel, out of the moors. He stole across the fens in the thick darkness, and touched the great iron bars of the door of the hall, which immediately sprang open. Then, with his eyes shooting out flame, he saw the knights sleeping after battle. With his steel fingernails the monster seized thirty of them in their sleep. He gave yells of joy, and sped as quick as lightning across the moors, to reach his home with his prey.

226

When the knights awoke, they raised a great cry of sorrow, while the aged king himself sat speechless with grief. None could do battle with the monster; he was too strong, too horrible for anyone to conquer. For twelve long years Grendel warred against Hrothgar. Like a dark shadow of death he prowled round about the hall, and lay in wait for his men on the misty moors. One thing he could not touch, and that was the king's sacred throne.

Now there lived in a far-off land a young man called Beowulf, who had the strength of thirty men. He heard of the wicked deeds of Grendel, and the sorrow of the good King Hrothgar. So he had made ready a strong ship, and with fourteen friends set sail to visit Hrothgar, as he was in need of help. The good ship flew over the swelling ocean like a bird. When the voyagers saw shining white cliffs before them, they knew their journey was at an end. They made fast their ship, grasped their weapons, and thanked God that they had had an easy voyage.

227

Now the guard saw them from a tower. He set off to the shore, riding on horseback, and swinging a huge lance.

"Who are you," he cried, "bearing arms and openly landing here? I am bound to know from whence you come before you make a step forward. Listen to my plain words, and hasten to answer me."

Beowulf made answer that they came as friends, to rid Hrothgar of his wicked enemy Grendel, and at that the guard led them on to guide them to the King's palace. Downhill they ran, with a rushing sound of voices and the clash of arms, until they saw the hall shining like gold against the sky. The guard motioned them straight to it, then, wheeling round on his horse, he said, "It is time for me to go. May the Father of All keep you in safety. For myself, I must guard the coast."

228

The street was paved with stone, and Beowulf's men marched along, following it to the hall, their armor shining in the sun and clanging as they went. They reached the terrace, where they set down their broad shields. Then they seated themselves on the bench, while they stacked their spears together and made themselves known to the herald.

Hrothgar speedily made them welcome. They entered the great hall, Beowulf leading the way. His armor shone like a golden network, and his look was high and noble, as he said, "Hail, O King! To fight against Grendel singlehanded have I come. Grant me this, that I may have this task alone, I and my little band of men. I know that the terrible monster uses no weapons, and therefore I shall bear neither sword, nor shield, nor buckler. Hand-to-hand I will fight him, and death shall come to whomsoever God wills. If death overtakes me, then will the monster carry away my body to the swamps, so care not for my body, but send my armor to my king. My fate is in God's hands."

Hrothgar loved the youth for his noble words, and asked him and his men to sit down to the table and merrily share the feast. The queen, in cloth of gold, moved down the hall and handed the jeweled cup of mead to the king and all the warriors, old and young. At the right moment, with kindly words, she brought it to Beowulf. Full of pride and high purpose, the youth drank from the splendid cup, and vowed that he would conquer the enemy or die.

When the sun sank in the west, all the guests arose. The king asked Beowulf to guard the house, and watch for Grendel. "Have courage," he said, "be watchful, resolve on success. Not a wish of yours shall be left unfulfilled, if you perform this mighty deed."

Then Beowulf lay down to rest in the hall, putting off from him his coat of mail, helmet, and sword.

Through the dim night Grendel came stealing. All slept in the darkness, all but one! The door sprang open at the first touch that the monster gave it. He stepped quickly over the paved floor of the hall; his eyes gleamed as he saw a troop of warriors lying together asleep. He laughed as he considered how he would take the life of each one before day broke. He seized a sleeping warrior, and in a flash had swallowed him.

Then he stretched out his hand to seize Beowulf on his bed. Quickly did Beowulf grip Grendel's arm; he stood up full length and struggled with him with all his might, till his fingers cracked as though they would burst. Never had Grendel felt such a grip; he had a mind to go, but could not. He roared, and the hall resounded with his yells, as up and down he raged, with Beowulf holding fast to him. The benches were overturned, the timbers of the hall cracked, the beautiful hall was all but wrecked.

Beowulf's men had seized their weapons and thought to strike Grendel on every side, but no blade could touch him. Still Beowulf held him by the arm. Grendel's shoulder cracked, and he fled, wounded to death, leaving hand, arm, and shoulder in Beowulf's grasp. Over the moors, into the darkness, he sped as best he might, and to Beowulf was the victory.

Then in the morning many a warrior came from far and near. Riding in troops, they tracked the monster's path, where he had fled wounded to death. In a dark and muddy pool he had yielded up his life.

Racing their horses over the green countryside, they reached again the paved street. The golden roof of the palace glittered in the sunlight. The king stood on the terrace and gave thanks

to God. "I have had much sorrow," he said, "but this lad through God's might has done the deed that we, with all our wisdom, could not do. Now I will heartily love you, Beowulf, as if you were my son. You shall want for nothing in this world, and your fame shall live forever."

The palace was put in order, the walls hung anew with cloth of gold, the whole place was made fair and straight, for only the roof had been left altogether unhurt after the fight.

A merry feast was held. The king brought forth out of his treasures a banner, helmet, and mail coat. These he gave to Beowulf; but more wonderful than all was a famous sword handed down to him through the ages. Then eight horses with golden cheekplates were brought within the court; one of them was saddled with King Hrothgar's own saddle, decorated with silver. Hrothgar gave all to Beowulf, bidding him enjoy them well. To each of Beowulf's men he gave rich gifts. The minstrels sang. The queen, beautiful and kind, bore the cup to the king and Beowulf. To Beowulf she, too, gave gifts—mantle and bracelets and collar of gold. "Use these gifts," she said, "and may all go well with you! As far as the sea rolls, your name shall be known."

Great was the joy of all till evening came. Then the hall was cleared of benches and the beds set out. Beowulf, like the king, had his own room this night to sleep in. The nobles lay down in the hall. At their heads they set their shields and placed ready their helmets and their mail coats. Each slept, ready in an instant to do battle for his lord.

So they sank to rest, little dreaming what deep sorrow was to fall on them.

Grendel the monster was dead, but Grendel's mother still lived. Wildly angry at the death of her son, she crept to the great hall, and made her way in, clutched a lord, the king's dearest friend, and crushed him in his sleep. Great was the uproar, though the terror was less than when Grendel came. The knights leapt up, sword in hand. The witch hurried to escape; she wanted to get out with her life.

The aged king felt terrible grief when he heard that his dearest friend was killed. He sent for Beowulf. The youth stood before Hrothgar and hoped that all was well.

"Do not ask if things go well," said the sorrowing king. "We have fresh grief this morning. My dearest friend and noblest knight is dead. Grendel you yourself destroyed through the strength given you by God, but another monster has come to avenge his death. I have heard the country folk say that there were two huge monsters to be seen stalking over the moors, one like a woman, as near as they could make out, the other with the form of a man, but huger and stronger by far. It was he they called Grendel. These two creatures haunt a fearful spot, a land of untrodden bogs and windy cliffs. A waterfall plunges into the blackness below, and twisted trees with outcropping roots overhang it. An unearthly fire is seen gleaming there night after night. None can tell the depth of the stream. · It is a fearful spot. You are our only help. Dare you enter this horrible haunt?"

Quick was Beowulf's answer: "Sorrow not, O King! Prepare yourself quickly, and let us track the monster. Each of us must look for death, and he who has the chance should do mighty deeds before it comes. I promise you Grendel's mother shall not escape me, if she hide in the depths of the earth or the ocean."

The king sprang up gladly, and Beowulf and his friends set out. They passed stony banks and high cliffs, the haunts of goblins.

Suddenly they saw a clump of gloomy trees, overhanging a dark pool. A shudder ran through them, for the pool was blood-red.

All sat down by the edge of the pool, while the horn sounded a cheerful blast. In the water were huge sea snakes, and on the points of land were dragons and strange beasts. They tumbled away, full of rage, at the sound of the horn.

234

One of Beowulf's men took aim at a monster with his arrow, and shot him through, so that he swam no more.

Beowulf was making ready for the fight. He covered his body with armor. On his head was a white helmet decorated with figures of boars worked in silver. No weapon could hurt it. His sword was a wondrous treasure, with an edge of iron. It had never failed anyone who needed it in battle.

"Be like a father to my men, if I perish," said Beowulf to Hrothgar, "and send the rich gifts you have given me to my king. He will see that I had good fortune while life lasted. Either I will win fame, or death shall take me."

He dashed away, plunging headlong into the pool. It took nearly the whole day before he reached the bottom, and while he was still on his way, the water-witch met him. For a hundred years she had lived in those depths. She made a grab at him, and caught him in her talons, but his coat of mail saved him from her dreadful fingers. Still she clutched him tightly, and bore him in her arms to the bottom of the lake. Beowulf had no power to use his weapons, though he had courage enough. Water beasts swam after him and battered him with their tusks.

Then he saw that he was in a huge hall, where there was no water, but a strange, unearthly glow of firelight. At once he began to fight, but the sword would not bite—it failed its master in his need; for the first time its fame broke down. Beowulf threw it away in anger, trusting to the strength of his hands. He cared nothing for his own life, for he thought but of honor.

He seized the witch by the shoulder and swayed her so that she sank to the floor. Quickly she recovered, and closed in on him. He staggered and fell, worn out. She sat on him, and drew her knife to take his life, but his good mail coat turned the point. He stood up again, and then truly God helped him, for he saw among the armor on the wall an old sword of huge size, the handiwork of giants. He seized it, and struck with all his might, so that the witch gave up her life.

Beowulf's heart was full of gladness. And light, calm and beautiful as that of the sun, filled the hall. He looked around the huge chamber, and saw Grendel lying there dead. He cut off his head as a trophy for King Hrothgar, whose men the monster had killed and devoured.

Now those men who were seated on the banks of the pool watching with Hrothgar saw that the water was colored with blood. Then the old men spoke together of the brave Beowulf, saying they feared that they would never see him alive again.

The day was going fast, so they and the king went homeward. Beowulf's men stayed on, sick at heart, gazing at the pool. They longed, but did not expect, to see their lord and master.

Under the depths, Beowulf was making his way to them. The magic sword melted in his hand, like snow in sunshine; only the hilt remained, so deadly was the monster that had been killed therewith. He brought nothing more with him than the hilt and Grendel's head. Up he rose through the waters where the angry sea beasts before had chased him. Now not one was to be seen. The depths were cleared when the witch lost her life. So he came to land, bravely swimming, bearing his spoils. His men saw him; they thanked God, and ran to free him of his armor.

Now they marched gladly through the highways to the town. It took four of them to carry Grendel's head. On they went, all fourteen, their captain glorious in their midst. They entered the great hall, startling the king and queen, as they sat at meat, with the fearful sight of Grendel's head.

Beowulf handed the magic hilt to Hrothgar, who saw that it was the work of giants of old. He spoke to Beowulf, while all held their peace, praised him for his courage, said that he would love him as his son, and bade him be a help to mankind, remembering not to glory in his own strength, for he held it from God. "Many treasures," he said, "must pass from me to you tomorrow, but now rest and feast."

When day dawned, Beowulf bade the king farewell, promising to help him again in time of need. Hrothgar, with tears and embraces, let him go, giving him fresh gifts of jewels. He wept, for he loved Beowulf well, and knew he would never see him any more.

Hamilton W. Mabie

Finding Words That Describe

This Anglo-Saxon legend tells of the mighty hero Beowulf, who braved great dangers to defeat wicked monsters and evil creatures. Throughout the story you will find words describing Beowulf. List some of these descriptions and be prepared to read them to the class.

What words are used to describe Grendel? Make an illustration of what this word picture suggests to you.

Find the description of the fearful spot where Grendel and his mother lived. What words make it particularly fearful?

The words *swamps*, *moors*, *fens*, and *bogs* create an atmosphere for the setting of this story. Explain what these words mean. Use your glossary if you need help.

Thinking About the Story

Why did Beowulf fight Grendel singlehanded and without weapons? Why was Beowulf strong enough to kill Grendel? Prepare to read aloud to the class the part that tells about Beowulf's fight with Grendel.

Who was the monster that came to avenge the death of Grendel? How did Beowulf's fight with Grendel differ from that with Grendel's mother? When did each take place? Where did each take place? What weapons did Beowulf use?

Taking Another Look

The story of Beowulf is written in a style not often used in modern stories. Reword the following phrases to read as you would say them today:

had made ready	putting off from him
sit down to table	yielded up his life
to do battle	prepare yourself quickly

The Making of the Hammer

THE VIKINGS believed that somewhere high above the earth there was a wonderful land peopled by gods. They called the land Asgard. The gods were much like the people on the earth below, only wiser and more beautiful. They possessed magic too. All the gods and goddesses were noble, though they did not always behave nobly. Sometimes they showed bad temper and meanness. One of these gods was bad all through. His name was Loki. He was a mischief maker and was fond of playing cruel tricks on the other gods.

One day as the goddess Sif was sitting in her palace in Asgard, she fell asleep. Sif was a beautiful goddess with long golden hair of which the god Thor, her husband, was very proud. Now as she lay sleeping, her golden hair fell about her shoulders in a shining glory. Loki happened to pass by the palace and saw Sif asleep with her lovely hair fallen about her, and he decided to cut it off. Quietly he tiptoed into the

240

palace, cut off the golden locks without wakening Sif, and hurried away with them. When Sif woke and found her beautiful hair gone, she ran and hid herself, for she feared Thor's anger.

Presently Thor came, but no Sif was there to meet him. She had never failed to greet him before, and the god, who was afraid of nothing on earth or in Asgard above it, now feared greatly that some ill had befallen his beloved Sif.

He ran from room to room of the palace searching for her. At last he found her hidden behind a tall column, her poor head bowed.

As Thor gazed down upon his wife's shorn head, his fury mounted in him until he bellowed with rage. The palace shook with his roars.

At last he said, "I know who did it. It was that wicked Loki, and I'll break every bone in his body."

Thor strode off in search of Loki, and when he had found him, he grabbed him by the neck and would have killed him then and there, but Loki begged for his life and promised to restore the stolen hair.

"I'll get the elves to make some hair for Sif more beautiful than her own," he gasped as the angry Thor held him tightly.

Thor cared more for Sif's beauty than for Loki's life, so he let him go on condition that he restore the golden hair as promised.

Loki lost no time, but went deep down into the earth to the home of the dwarfs. There at their gloomy smithy were Ivald's sons, wonderful workers in gold and brass.

"Make me a crown of golden hair," said Loki, "that will grow like any other hair, and I will give you whatever you want for your work."

242

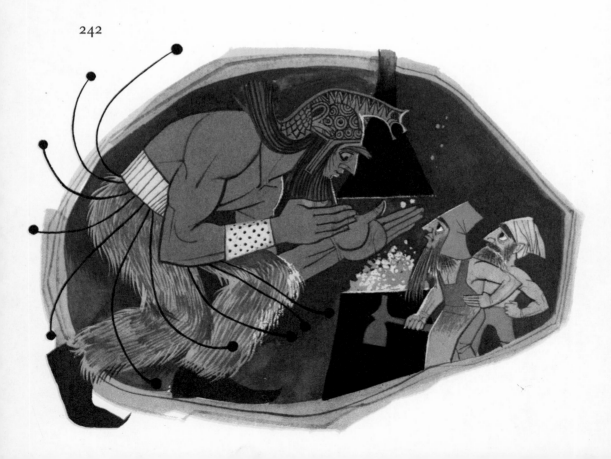

The bargain was quickly made, and the busy little dwarfs were soon at work. In very short time they had done all that Loki asked, and more too. Along with the shining hair they gave Loki the spear Gungner and the famous ship Skidbladner.

With these treasures in his arms Loki came into Asgard and boasted of the wonderful things he had brought from the smithy. "No one can work in metal like the sons of Ivald," he declared. "The other dwarfs are stupid compared with them."

Now it happened that the dwarf Brok was standing by and heard Loki's boasting. His brother Sindre was so cunning a workman that most of the dwarfs thought him by far the best in the world. It made Brok angry, therefore, to hear the sons of Ivald called the best workmen. So he spoke up and said, "My brother Sindre can make more wonderful things of gold and iron and brass than ever the sons of Ivald thought of."

"Your brother Sindre," repeated Loki scornfully. "Who is your brother Sindre?"

"The best workman in the world," answered Brok.

Loki laughed loud and long. "Go to your wonderful brother Sindre," he said, "and tell him if he can make three such precious things as the spear, the ship. and the golden hair, he shall have my head for his trouble."

Brok was off to the underworld before Loki's laughter had died away, determined to have Loki's head if magic and hard work could do it. He went straight to Sindre and told him of the wager he had laid with Loki, and in a little while Sindre was hard at work in his smithy. It was a queer place for such wonderful work as was done in it, for it was nothing but a great cavern underground, with tools piled up in little heaps around its sides, and thick darkness everywhere when the furnace fire was not sending its glow out into the blackness.

243

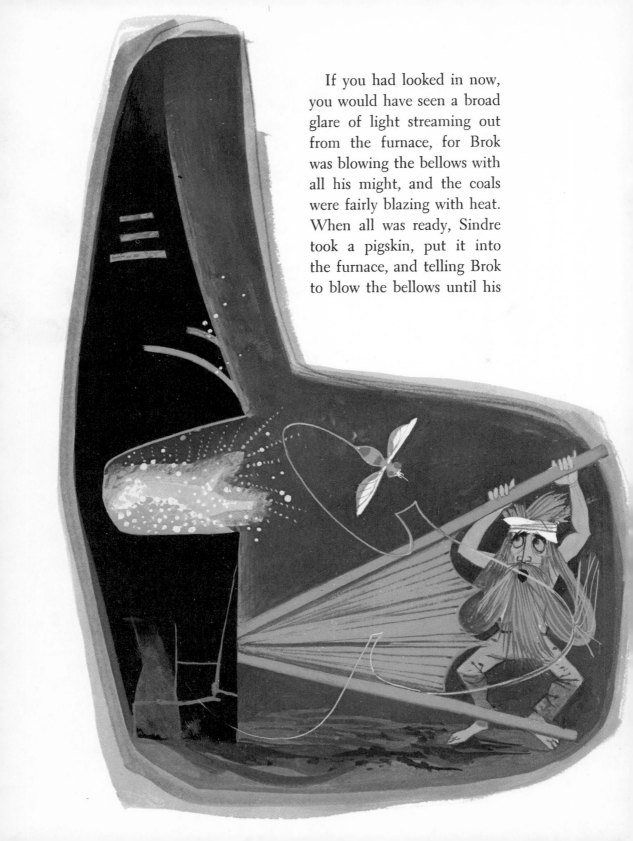

If you had looked in now, you would have seen a broad glare of light streaming out from the furnace, for Brok was blowing the bellows with all his might, and the coals were fairly blazing with heat. When all was ready, Sindre took a pigskin, put it into the furnace, and telling Brok to blow the bellows until his return, went out of the smithy. Brok kept steadily at his work although a gadfly flew in and buzzed noisily about. The gadfly was of course Loki, who had the power of taking any shape he wanted. At last the gadfly settled on Brok's hand and stung him so that he could hardly bear it. After a while Sindre came back and took out of the furnace a wonderful boar with bristles of pure gold.

Then Sindre took some gold, and placing it in the furnace, told Brok to blow as if his life depended on it, and went out a second time. Brok had no sooner begun blowing than the troublesome gadfly came back. This time he fastened upon Brok's neck and stung him so fiercely that he could hardly keep his hands away from his neck. But Brok was a faithful dwarf, who meant to do his work well if he died for it. So he worked the bellows as if it were the easiest thing in the world. Presently Sindre came back and took a shining ring from the fire.

The third time Sindre put iron into the fire and told Brok to work without stopping even once. Then he went out again. No sooner had he gone than the gadfly flew in and settled between Brok's eyes. He stung him so sharply that drops of blood ran down into his eyes, and he could not see what he was doing. He worked the bellows as bravely as he could for some time, but the pain was so keen and he was so blind that at last he raised his hand quickly to brush the fly away. That very instant Sindre returned.

"You have almost spoiled it," he said as he took out of the glowing furnace the wonderful hammer Mjolner. "See how short you have made the handle. But you can't lengthen it now. So carry the gifts to Asgard, and bring me Loki's head."

Brok started off with the golden boar, the shining ring, and the terrible hammer.

When he came through the great gate of Asgard, the gods were very anxious to see the end of this strange contest. Taking their seats on their shining thrones, they appointed Odin, All Father of the Gods, Thor, and Freya, Odin's wife, to judge whose gifts were best—those of Loki or the ones belonging to Brok. Then Loki brought out the spear Gungner, which never missed its mark, and gave it to Odin. The golden hair he gave to Thor, who placed it on Sif's head, and straightway it began to grow like any other hair. Sif was as beautiful as on the day when Loki saw her in Thor's palace and robbed her of her hair. To Freya, Loki gave the ship Skidbladner, which always found a breeze to drive it wherever its master would go, no matter how the sea was running or from what direction the wind was blowing, and which could be folded up and carried in one's pocket.

Then Loki laughed scornfully. "Bring out the trinkets which that wonderful brother of yours has made," he said.

Brok came forward and stood before the wondering gods with his treasure.

"This ring," said he, handing it to Odin, "will cast off, every ninth night, eight other rings as pure and heavy as itself. This boar," he said, giving it to Freya, "will run more swiftly in the air and on the sea, by night or by day, than the swiftest horse, and no night will be so dark, no world so gloomy, that the shining of these bristles shall not make it light as noonday. And this hammer," placing Mjolner in Thor's strong hands, "will never fail, no matter how big nor how hard that which it strikes may be. No matter how far it is thrown, it will always return to your hand. You may make it so small that it can be hidden in your sleeve, and its only fault is the shortness of its handle."

247

Thor swung it around his head, and lightning flashed and flamed through Asgard, deep peals of thunder rolled through the sky, and mighty masses of clouds piled quickly up around him. The gods gathered around and passed the hammer from one to another, saying that it would be their greatest protection against their enemies, the frost-giants, who were always trying to force their way into Asgard. They therefore declared that Brok had won the wager.

Brok's face shone as bright as his brother's furnace fire, so delighted was he to have beaten Loki. But how was he to get his wager now he had won it? It was no easy matter to take the head off a god's shoulders. Brok thought a moment.

"I will take Loki's head," he said finally, thinking some of the other gods might help him.

"I will give you whatever you want in place of my head," growled Loki, angry that he was beaten and having no idea of paying his wager by losing his head.

"I will have your head or I will have nothing," answered the brave little dwarf, determined not to be cheated of his victory.

"Well, then, take it," shouted Loki. But by the time Brok reached the place where he had been standing, Loki was far away, for he wore shoes with which he could run through the air or over the water. Then Brok asked Thor to find Loki and bring him back, which Thor did promptly, for the gods always saw to it that people kept their promises. When Loki was brought back, Brok wanted to cut his head off at once.

"You may cut off my head, but you have no right to touch my neck," said Loki, who was cunning as well as wicked. That was true, and of course the head could not be taken off without touching the neck, so Brok had to give it up.

A Norse Myth

248

Thinking About the Story

This story is a Norse myth told by the Vikings. What does the word Norse mean? Who were the Vikings? Read in an encyclopedia or reference book and tell the group some interesting facts about them.

The first paragraph sets the stage for the story. Skim the paragraph to find where it takes place and who is the main character. What sentence hints of what is to happen?

The story says that Sindre's smithy was a queer place. What is a smithy? Be ready to read the description of this smithy to the group.

How did Loki try to spoil Brok's work? Why do you think he did not succeed?

The story tells much about Brok and Loki. What kind of people were they? Which one do you think was the more clever? Why? Which one showed determination? How?

If you had been a judge, which of the six things would you have chosen as being the most wonderful? Why?

Thor has been called the God of Thunder. What connection do you see between his title and something which he did in the story?

Giving a Play

"The Making of the Hammer" is a good story to make into a play. You will want to make a list of the scenes and characters, and to decide what the characters will do and say.

Who will be in the first scene besides Sif? What will each person say? How will each one act? Will you need a narrator to tell part of the story? What will you need for scenery and props? You may wish to have tryouts to select the cast for your play.

249

The Pied Piper

Cast

ANNOUNCER	PIPER
NARRATOR	FRANZ
GIRL	MOTHER
BOY	FIRST COUNCILOR
MAYOR	SECOND COUNCILOR
SENTRY	FIRST WOMAN
FIRST MAN	SECOND WOMAN
SECOND MAN	THIRD WOMAN

Sounds

Music	Door open
Sound of pipe	Door shut
Church bells	Knock at door

250

ANNOUNCER. Hello, boys and girls. It's story time. This tale you will hear comes from Germany. It tells about some people who didn't keep a promise and how they were punished. Listen to "The Pied Piper."

MUSIC. (*Up and out*)

NARRATOR. There wasn't a prettier town in all Germany than the little town of Hamelin. A deep river flowed past the town, and a tall tree-covered mountain at its back kept the harsh winds away. It was a very pleasant place to live. But at one time, over five hundred years ago, the people of Hamelin were leading most uncomfortable lives. Why? Well, because Hamelin was overrun by rats.

GIRL. Rats! They fought the dogs and killed the cats,

BOY. And bit the babies in their cradles,

GIRL. And ate the cheeses out of the vats,

BOY. And licked the soup from the cooks' own ladles.

GIRL. Split open the kegs of salted sprats,

BOY. Made nests inside men's Sunday hats,

GIRL. And even spoiled the women's chats,
By drowning their speaking
With shrieking and squeaking
In fifty different sharps and flats.

MUSIC. (*Short bridge*)

NARRATOR. Yes, that was what made the people of Hamelin so miserable—the rats. In their homes and at their work the people suffered from the great number of rats that walked boldly through the streets and houses. There seemed to be no way of killing them off or driving them out.

One day as the Mayor was sitting at his desk in the Town Hall, there was a knock at the door. (*Fade*) He called out—

MAYOR. Come in!

SOUND. (*Door open*)

MAYOR. What is it, sentry?

SENTRY. There are two men outside, your Honor, who say they must speak to you.

MAYOR. What about?

SENTRY. I don't know, your Honor. They say they were chosen by the people to call on you.

MAYOR. Very well, sentry. Show them in. (*Short pause*) Good morning, gentlemen. Come in and have a seat.

SOUND. (*Door shut*)

FIRST MAN. Thank you, your Honor.

MAYOR. Now, what can I do for you, gentlemen?

FIRST MAN. The people of Hamelin have sent us to speak for them on a most important matter.

MAYOR. And what is this most important matter?

SECOND MAN. The rats, Mr. Mayor. You must rid Hamelin of the rats that make life miserable for us.

MAYOR. The rats again! The Town Councilors and I have tried to get rid of them.

FIRST MAN. Then you must try harder. We elected you to make the town a good place to live in.

MAYOR. We have made Hamelin a safe place to live by driving away all thieves and other bad men.

SECOND MAN. True. But these rats are worse than any thieves. They will force us to leave our homes and go to another town to live if you don't do something about them soon.

MAYOR. But, gentlemen, we have done our best.

FIRST MAN. That is not good enough. The people chose you and the Town Councilors because we believed you were wise men. We are tired of paying our good money to town officials who don't know how to get rid of rats.

MAYOR. We have done everything possible. There never were such big, fierce, and fearless rats!

SECOND MAN. The people believe it is your duty to find a way to get rid of the rats. If you can't, *we* will get rid of *you* and choose men with better brains.

MAYOR. But, gentlemen—!

FIRST MAN. The people sent us here to warn you. Either you rid us of these pests, or Hamelin will have a new Mayor and a new group of Town Councilors. Good morning, your Honor!

SOUND. (*Door open and shut noisily*)

MAYOR. Dear me! What a mess this is! (*Calls*) Sentry!

SOUND. (*Door open quietly*)

SENTRY. Yes, your Honor?

MAYOR. You hear the people talking as you walk about the town. Do you think the people really mean this talk about a new Mayor?

SENTRY. The people are very much upset by this time, your Honor, and they are likely to do anything to get rid of the rats.

MAYOR. My head aches with trying to think.

SOUND. (*Gentle knock at door*)

MAYOR. What's that? Is that a knock at the door or a rat? Anything that sounds like a rat makes my heart go pitapat.

SOUND. (*Knock repeated*)

SENTRY. I'll see who it is, sir.

MAYOR. Let him in, whoever he is. Well, bless my soul! What a strange figure of a man! Tall and thin as a bean pole. Shut the door, sentry, but remain on guard.

SOUND. (*Door shut*)

MAYOR. You dress in a queer fashion, stranger. Your clothes are half yellow, half red, like the king's jester in my grandfather's time.

PIPER. That is why men call me the Pied Piper, because of the different colors of my clothing.

MAYOR. Why have you come to Hamelin? What is it you want of me?

PIPER. If you please, Mr. Mayor, I have come to rid your town of its rats.

MAYOR. What! Did I hear you correctly? Did you say you have come to rid us of the rats?

254

PIPER. Yes, your Honor. I know I can do it.

MAYOR. How? Have you a special poison or a new trap?

PIPER. Neither. I am able, by a secret charm, to make all living things follow me—all creatures that creep or swim or fly or run.

MAYOR. And do you use this secret charm on any living things, whenever you feel like it?

PIPER. Oh, no, your Honor. I use it only on creatures that harm people. You see this pipe tied to the red-and-yellow scarf around my neck?

MAYOR. Yes, and I can see that your fingers are impatient to pick it up and play on it.

PIPER. By playing a tune on this pipe of mine, I have rid other towns of mice and rats and other harmful creatures. I can rid Hamelin of its rats, too, if you will pay the price I ask.

MAYOR. If you will free Hamelin of its rats, the Town Council will gladly pay you any price you ask.

PIPER. For this service I ask one thousand guilders, your Honor.

MAYOR. One thousand guilders! I will be glad to pay you fifty thousand out of the town money if you can do away with these pests.

PIPER. One thousand guilders is all I ask. Is it a bargain, your Honor?

MAYOR. It is a bargain, Piper. How happy we'll all be to see the rats leaving Hamelin!

MUSIC. (Sound of pipe up and fade out under narrator's speech)

NARRATOR. The Pied Piper smiled, and his blue eyes twinkled. He stepped into the street. He put his pipe to his lips and played a strange sweet tune. Before he had blown

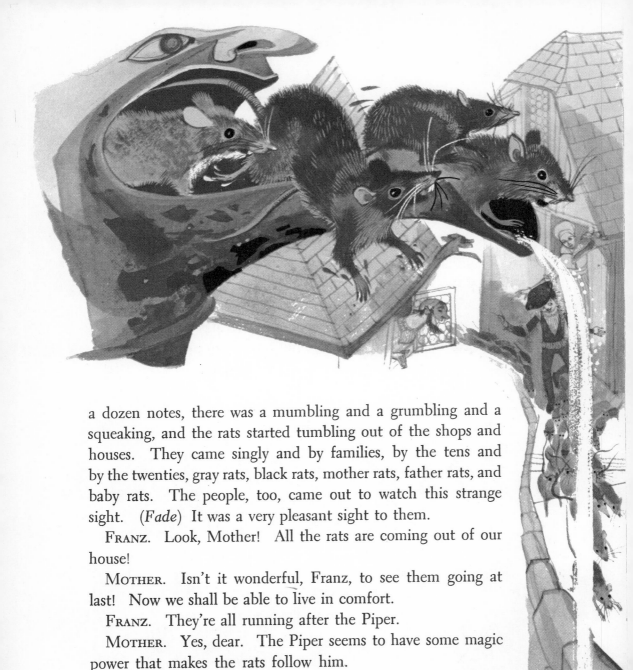

a dozen notes, there was a mumbling and a grumbling and a squeaking, and the rats started tumbling out of the shops and houses. They came singly and by families, by the tens and by the twenties, gray rats, black rats, mother rats, father rats, and baby rats. The people, too, came out to watch this strange sight. (*Fade*) It was a very pleasant sight to them.

FRANZ. Look, Mother! All the rats are coming out of our house!

MOTHER. Isn't it wonderful, Franz, to see them going at last! Now we shall be able to live in comfort.

FRANZ. They're all running after the Piper.

MOTHER. Yes, dear. The Piper seems to have some magic power that makes the rats follow him.

FRANZ. Let's follow along, Mother, and see where he takes the rats.

256

MOTHER. Walk slowly, dear. Be careful of your weak leg.

FRANZ. Do rats really like music so much?

MOTHER. I don't know. But this is surely a magic tune the Piper is playing for them.

FRANZ. I wonder what the rats hear in that song.

MOTHER. Well, I suppose that it sings to them of cupboard doors left open and shelves full of everything rats love to eat.

FRANZ. Shelves full of cheese and apples and bacon?

MOTHER. And open jars of peas and beans and, perhaps, some prunes.

FRANZ. And no cat to scare them away.

MOTHER. That must be a rat's idea of heaven!

FRANZ. I wonder where the Piper is taking them, Mother.

MOTHER. He's turning down this street. It leads to the river. Look, dear! He's going right down to the bank of the river! The rats are following him!

FRANZ. He's going to drown them!

MOTHER. Yes! The Piper is stepping aside, and—the rats are keeping straight on into the river!

FRANZ. The river is full of rats. They're drowning, every one of them! No more rats! Hurrah!

SOUND. (*Church bells up and under mother's speech*)

MOTHER. Listen! The church bells are ringing! It's a great day for Hamelin! The rats are gone! Let's go to the square in front of the Town Hall, Franz. Everybody will be going there.

SOUND. (*Church bells up full and out*)

VOICES. Hurrah! The rats are gone! The town is free of rats at last! The rats are gone! Hurrah!

MAYOR. (*Above voices*) People of Hamelin! (*Voices out*) People of Hamelin! Go back to your houses and make them clean and safe again. Clear out the nests where the rats have lived. Fill up the holes in the walls. Let there be no trace left in all Hamelin of the pests that almost drove us from our homes.

VOICES. Hurrah! No more rats in our homes! Three cheers for the Mayor! Hurrah! Hurrah! Hurrah!

MAYOR. Thank you, my good people.

PIPER. If you please, your Honor—

MAYOR. Who is interrupting my speech? Oh, it's you, the Pied Piper.

PIPER. Yes, your Honor. It's time for my—

MAYOR. You did a good job of getting rid of the rats.

PIPER. I told you I would. And now, if you please, my thousand guilders.

MAYOR. A thousand guilders. Ahem! That's a very large sum of money.

PIPER. You promised it if I would get rid of the rats.

MAYOR. But a thousand guilders! I'll ask my Town Councilors here at my side. What do you say, Councilors?

FIRST COUNCILOR. That is a very high price to pay a man, your Honor, just for playing a tune on a pipe.

SECOND COUNCILOR. (Low) Your Honor, think how much food we could buy for our Council dinners with half that sum.

MAYOR. You're right, Councilor. Why should we pay a thousand guilders to this beggar?

FIRST COUNCILOR. Besides, your Honor, the rats are gone now. We saw them drown. The Piper played them into the river, but he can't play them alive again.

MAYOR. That makes sense, Councilor. He cannot bring them back to life. They're gone forever.

FIRST COUNCILOR. Then offer the Piper a small sum for his trouble, your Honor, and send him away.

PIPER. I'm waiting, your Honor, for my thousand guilders.

MAYOR. Surely you don't expect me to give you all that money, Piper.

PIPER. That was our bargain. One thousand guilders.

MAYOR. But I never meant it. I was only jesting.

PIPER. Oh, no, you were not jesting, your Honor. You were so anxious for me to get rid of those rats that you offered me fifty thousand. But I won't ask for that, only for the one thousand I asked at the time.

MAYOR. But we can't pay that much money. The rats have done so much damage that we need a great deal of money to repair our buildings.

PIPER. You are wasting my time, Mr. Mayor. I must be on my way to Persia. I have an appointment with the Sultan of Bagdad. Give me my thousand guilders for the service I have performed for your town.

MAYOR. We'll give you fifty guilders.

PIPER. I carried out my part of the bargain and got rid of the rats for you. Now you must keep yours and pay me the money you promised.

MAYOR. I tell you I was only joking. Take the fifty guilders and be off.

PIPER. Not a copper less than the thousand will I take, your Honor. If you make me angry, I'll pipe another tune, and you'll be sorry.

MAYOR. What! Do you dare to threaten me, the Mayor of Hamelin? You, a beggar with only a pipe and a red-and-yellow suit of clothes to your name?

PIPER. All I am asking is that you keep your promise.

MAYOR. The rats are gone forever, drowned in the river. Suppose I refuse to pay you anything at all now?

PIPER. I tell you, your Honor, if you do that, I'll play a tune that will make you sorry the rest of your life.

MAYOR. Play your tune, then! Do your worst! Not one guilder shall you get!

PIPER. Very well, Mr. Mayor. I gave you fair warning.

MUSIC. (*Sound of pipe up and fade under narrator's speech*)

NARRATOR. The Pied Piper left the Town Hall Square. Once more he put his pipe to his lips. This time the music was soft and sweet, yet merry too. The Piper had no sooner started playing when along came the children, skipping and laughing and clapping their hands with delight.

SOUND. (*Laughter of children in briefly and fade out*)

NARRATOR. The bright-eyed little girls with their golden curls, the rose-cheeked boys, all danced after the Piper as he played his wonderful music. At first the people laughed, too, when they saw their children dancing so gaily. But soon the parents began to grow frightened. (*Fade*) They called after the children.

MOTHER. Come back, Franz! Come back here!

FIRST WOMAN. Gretchen, darling! Come back to Mother!

262

SECOND WOMAN. Otto! Otto! Don't follow the Piper! Come back here! Come back!

THIRD WOMAN. Some of you men, run after the children! Make them turn back! Take them away from the Piper!

FIRST MAN. I can't move!

SECOND MAN. I can't, either! The Piper has bewitched us!

MOTHER. Mayor, send your police to make the Piper bring our children back!

MAYOR. None of us can stir a step. The Piper has bewitched us all! My own children, too, are following after him.

FIRST WOMAN. Where is he taking our children?

SECOND WOMAN. He's turning down the street to the river! He'll drown our children as he drowned the rats!

MAYOR. Oh, why didn't we pay him the money? What's a thousand guilders compared to our children?

FIRST WOMAN. Look! The Piper is turning away from the river. He's going toward the mountain!

SECOND WOMAN. Then our children are safe! They will never be able to climb over the top.

THIRD WOMAN. The Piper will have to stop playing, and our children will come back to us.

FIRST MAN. Look! The mountain is opening! A door in the side of the mountain is opening!

FIRST WOMAN. Our children are following the Piper inside the mountain. Come back, children!

VOICES. The mountain is opening! The Piper is leading the children inside the mountain! Oh! Oh! Come back, children. Can't you hear us? Come back!

264

MAYOR. The mountain has shut fast! We shall never see our children again! Why didn't we pay the Piper? Why didn't we keep our promise?

VOICES. (*Despairing*) Oh! Oh! Our children! Our children are gone!

MUSIC. (*Bridge*)

NARRATOR. But not all the children had disappeared inside the mountain. As the people of Hamelin stood weeping and staring in horror at the mountain, a little boy limped slowly back to the Square. It was Franz, the carpenter's little lame boy. (*Fade*) His mother hugged him tightly to her.

MOTHER. Franz, my darling! How happy I am to have you back! You're a good boy for not going with the others.

FRANZ. I wanted to go with the other children, Mother. I didn't want to come back here.

MOTHER. But you heard me calling and you listened. You didn't go inside the mountain with the Piper.

FRANZ. I didn't hear anyone calling. I heard only the lovely things that the Piper's music promised me. I didn't go inside with the others because I am lame. (*Weeping*) I couldn't walk fast enough. The door in the mountain shut before I could get inside.

MOTHER. Oh, my darling! For once I am happy that you are lame. What did the Piper's music promise you?

FRANZ. It sang of a lovely land where everything was strange and beautiful, where the grass was carpeted with bright flowers, and the trees were full of sweet fruits. There the sparrows were as large and beautiful as peacocks, and the honeybees had no stings. And just as the music was promising me that my lame foot would be well again and I could run and play like the other children, the door of the mountain closed, and I was left outside. (*Weeps*) And now I'll never see that beautiful land, and my foot will never be well!

MOTHER. Oh, my little Franz!

MAYOR. The little Franz is the only child left in Hamelin.

FRANZ. I'll never see my playmates again! I'll have nobody to play with! I wish I had gone with the Piper!

MAYOR. People of Hamelin! Today we have been taught a lesson that we shall never forget. How costly a broken promise may be! Let us write this sad story so that others born after us may read it and know that a promise given must always be kept.

MUSIC. (*Bridge*)

NARRATOR. And so the people of Hamelin wrote the story of the Pied Piper and the lost children of Hamelin on a stone column. They placed the column opposite the spot where the mountain had opened. On the windows of the church they painted pictures of their children following the Piper. And they say that after that, no man or woman of Hamelin ever broke a promise.

MUSIC. (*Up full and out*)

ANNOUNCER. And so ends the story of the man who could charm animals and children with the music of his magic pipe.

Fan Kissen

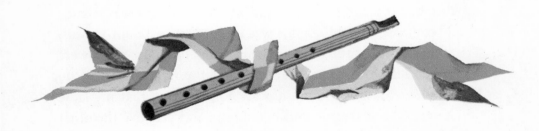

Thinking About the Story

Explain the meaning of the name *Pied Piper*. What was the Piper's secret charm? On what could it be used?

Why was little Franz so unhappy? What had the Piper's music promised him? Write a paragraph telling what the Piper's music might have promised you if you had been one of the children of Hamelin.

What reasons did the mayor give for not paying the Piper the full amount promised to him? Why did the mayor feel safe in not keeping his promise? Do you think the Piper really did give a "fair warning"?

What did the people of Hamelin learn as a result of this experience? Why was this such a costly lesson? What lesson did you learn as you read the play? Why do you think that *a promise given must always be kept?* Be prepared to discuss it with the class.

Planning and Giving the Play

It would be fun to make your classroom into a broadcasting station and present the radio play "The Pied Piper." What would you need for the broadcast?

Skim the play for sound and stage directions. How will you make the necessary sounds? Perhaps you will wish to have a sound-effects man.

If you are not sure of the meaning of *up, out, bridge,* and *fade* look in the glossary.

Look at the list of characters and try to interpret some of the parts before choosing the cast for the play.

After the play is given, make a list of the things that made it most interesting and real.

The Good Joan

Along the thousand roads of France,
Now there, now here, swift as a glance,
A cloud, a mist blown down the sky,
Good Joan of Arc goes riding by.

In Domremy at candlelight,
The orchards blowing rose and white
About the shadowy houses lie;
And Joan of Arc goes riding by.

On Avignon there falls a hush,
Brief as the singing of a thrush
Across old gardens April-high;
And Joan of Arc goes riding by.

The women bring the apples in,
Round Arles when the long gusts begin,
Then sit them down to sob and cry;
And Joan of Arc goes riding by.

Dim fall the hoofs down old Calais;
In Tours a flash of silver-gray,
Like flaw of rain in a clear sky;
And Joan of Arc goes riding by.

Who saith that ancient France shall fail,
A rotting leaf driv'n down the gale?
Then her sons know not how to die;
Then good God dwells no more on high!

Tours, Arles, and Domremy reply!
For Joan of Arc goes riding by.

     Lizette Woodworth Reese

Chanticleer and the Fox

ONCE UPON A TIME a poor widow, getting on in years, lived in a small cottage beside a grove which stood in a little valley. This widow, about whom I shall tell you my tale, had patiently led a very simple life since the day her husband died. By careful management she was able to take care of herself and her two daughters.

She had only three large hogs, three cows, and a sheep. Her bedroom was very sooty, as was her kitchen in which she ate many a scanty meal. She was never sick from overeating. Her table was usually set with only white and black—milk and dark bread, of which there was no shortage—and sometimes there was bacon and an egg or two, for she was, as it were, a kind of dairywoman.

She had a yard, fenced all around with sticks, in which she had a rooster named Chanticleer. For crowing, there was not his equal in all the land. His voice was merrier than the merry organ that plays in church, and his crowing from his resting place was more trustworthy than a clock. His comb was redder than fine coral and turreted like a castle wall, his bill was black and shone like jet, and his legs and toes were like azure. His nails were whiter than the lily, and his feathers were like burnished gold.

Now this fine rooster had seven hens, all colored like him. The hen with the prettiest throat was called fair Demoiselle Partlet. She was polite, discreet, debonair, and companionable, and she had conducted herself so well since the time that she was seven days old that, truly, she held the heart of Chanticleer all tightly locked. It was a great joy to hear them sing in sweet harmony when the bright sun began to rise. For in those days, so I'm told, beasts and birds could talk and sing.

And so it happened, one day at dawn, as Chanticleer sat on his perch surrounded by the hens, that he began to groan in his throat like a man troubled by his dreams. When Partlet heard him moaning this way, she was frightened and said, "Dear heart, what is it, that you groan in such a manner?"

And he answered, saying, "Madam, I dreamed just now that I was in much danger. I dreamed that I was roaming up and down within our yard, when I saw a beast like a hound which tried to grab my body and would have killed me. His color was between yellow and red, and his tail and both ears were tipped with black, different from the rest of his fur. His snout was small, and his two eyes glowed. I almost died of fear at the sight of him; doubtless that's what caused my groaning."

"Go on!" she said. "Shame on you. You know I cannot love a coward! Haven't you a man's heart and haven't you a beard? Be merry, husband. Do not fear dreams."

"Thank you, Madam Partlet," he said, "for your learned advice. I do say that when I see the beauty of your face all scarlet red about the eyes, my fears die away."

With these words he flew down from the perch, along with all the hens, for it was day. With a clucking he called them all to some grain which he found lying about the yard. He was as regal as a prince in his palace and was no longer afraid. He looked like a lion as he roamed up and down on his toes, barely setting foot to the earth.

Chanticleer, walking in all his pride, with his seven wives beside him, cast up his eyes at the bright sun. He crowed with a happy voice, "Listen how the happy birds sing, and how the fresh flowers grow. My heart is full of gaiety and joy."

But suddenly a sorrowful event overtook him.

A fox, tipped with black, and full of sly wickedness, had lived in the grove three years. That same night he burst through the hedges into the yard where fair Chanticleer and his wives were in the habit of going. And this fox lay quietly in a bed of herbs until almost noon of that day.

Partlet, with all her sisters nearby, lay merrily bathing in the sand, with her back to the sun, and the lordly Chanticleer sang more joyfully than the mermaid in the sea.

Now it happened that, as he cast his eye upon a butterfly among the herbs, Chanticleer became aware of the fox lying low. He had no desire to crow then, but at once cried, "Cok! Cok!" and started up like a man frightened in his heart.

He would have fled at once, if the fox had not said, "My dear sir, alas, where are you going? Are you afraid of me, your father's friend? The reason I came was only to listen to you sing. For, truly, you have as merry a voice as any angel in heaven. My lord your father—God bless his soul—and also

your courteous mother did me the great honor of visiting my house. Except for you I have never heard anyone who could sing as your father did in the morning. In order to make his voice stronger, he would close both his eyes. And he would stand on his tiptoes and stretch forth his long slender neck. Now sing, sir, for holy charity. Let's see whether you can sing as well as your father."

Chanticleer began to beat his wings. He stood high on his toes and stretched his neck, closed his eyes, and crowed loudly. At once the fox jumped up, grabbed Chanticleer by the throat, and carried him toward the woods.

Alas, that Chanticleer flew down from his perch! Alas, that his wife took no heed of dreams! And all this trouble came on a Friday.

Such a cry was never made as was made by all the hens in the yard when they saw Chanticleer captured. The poor widow and her two daughters heard the woeful cries of the hens and at once ran out of doors. They saw the fox going toward the grove, carrying away the rooster. "Help! Help! Woe is me! Look, a fox!" they screamed and ran after him.

The cows, the sheep, and even the hogs, so frightened were they by the shouting, ran after him too. They ran so hard they thought their hearts would burst.

The neighbors' ducks quacked as if they were to be killed; and their geese, from fear, flew over the trees; the noise was so terrible that the bees swarmed from their hive. It seemed that heaven would fall.

Now, good people, I beg you all to listen. This rooster in the fox's mouth spoke to the fox in spite of his fear, saying, "Sir, if I were you, so help me God, I would say, 'Turn back, you proud peasants! I have reached the edge of the wood now; the rooster shall stay here. In spite of you I will eat him, in faith, and not be long about it.'"

274

"In faith," the fox answered, "it shall be done." As soon as he spoke the words, the rooster nimbly broke away from his mouth and flew at once high into a tree.

When the fox saw that the rooster was gone, he said, "Alas! Oh, Chanticleer, alas! I have done you a bad turn. I frightened you when I grabbed you and took you out of the yard. But, sir, I did it without evil intent. Come down, and I shall tell you what I meant."

"Nay, then," said Chanticleer. "Never again shall you with your flattery get me to sing with my eyes closed. For he who closes his eyes when he should watch, God let him never prosper."

"No," said the fox, "but God bring misfortune to him who is so careless about his self-control as to prattle when he should hold his peace."

"See," said the widow as the fox slunk into the grove, "that is the result of trusting in flattery."

And she marched with her flock back to the yard in the little valley.

Adapted by Barbara Cooney
from The Canterbury Tales
by Geoffrey Chaucer

Looking Beyond the Story

Geoffrey Chaucer, the Father of English Poetry, wrote *The Canterbury Tales*. The book tells of a group of people traveling from London to Canterbury. To pass the time they entertained each other by telling stories. "Chanticleer and the Fox" is one of these stories.

The word *Chanticleer* comes from the French words meaning *clear singer*. Find another definition in your glossary. Why are both definitions suitable to this story?

Chanticleer and the fox both were tricked by flattery, and they each learned a lesson. What was it? What is the moral of the story?

Planning to Give a Puppet Show

This story would make a good puppet show. Who are the characters? What will they say?

The first scene might tell of Chanticleer's dream. The second could tell of his meeting with the fox. What might the third scene be about?

Decide how you will make your puppets. Keep the description of Chanticleer and the other animals in mind as you make your puppets.

276

The Fox

The fox set out in a hungry plight,
And begged the moon to give him light,
For he'd many a mile to travel that night,
Before he could reach his den O!

First he came to a farmer's yard,
Where the ducks and the geese declared it was hard
That their nerves should be shaken, and their rest be marred
By a visit from Mr. Fox O!

He seized the gray goose by the sleeve.
Says he, "Madam Gray Goose, by your leave,
I'll carry you off without reprieve,
And take you away to my den O!"

He seized the gray duck by the neck,
And flung her across his back,
While the old duck cried out, "Quack, quack, quack,"
With her legs dangling down behind O!

Then old Mrs. Flipper Flapper jumped out of bed,
And out of the window she popped her head,
Crying, "John, John, John, the gray goose is gone,
And the fox is off to his den O!"

Then John went up to the top of the hill,
And he blew a blast both loud and shrill.
Says the fox, "That is fine music, still
I'd rather be off to my den O!"

So the fox he hurried off to his den,
To his dear little foxes eight, nine, ten.
Says he, "We're in luck, here's a big fat duck
With her legs dangling down behind O!"

Then the fox sat down with his hungry wife,
And they made a good meal without fork or knife.
They never had a better time in all their life,
And the little ones picked the bones O!

Old Rhyme

Singing Words

Words can sing. You will find music in the words of a poem, for poems, like music, are meant to be heard and can be enjoyed over and over again.

The poems on these pages are especially for you. Some of them will be enjoyed just for their rhythm and the sounds of the words. Some will tell stories. Others will say in a very special way something you yourself have long felt. Still others will bring beauty and enchantment just for you alone. All this will come to you through the music of words—the words of poetry.

I KNOW how poems come;
They have wings.
When you are not thinking of it,
I suddenly say,
"Mother, a poem!"
Somehow I hear it
Rustling.

Poems come like boats
With sails for wings;
Crossing the sky swiftly
They slip under tall bridges
Of cloud.

Hilda Conkling

Sounds in Words

Some poems are enjoyed just for the sound of the words, rather than for their meaning. You will want to read these poems aloud so that you can really hear the sounds.

The Rum Tum Tugger

The Rum Tum Tugger is a Curious Cat:
If you offer him pheasant he would rather have grouse.
If you put him in a house he would much prefer a flat,
If you put him in a flat then he'd rather have a house.
If you set him on a mouse then he only wants a rat,
If you set him on a rat then he'd rather chase a mouse.
Yes the Rum Tum Tugger is a Curious Cat—
    And there isn't any call for me to shout it:
        For he will do
        As he do do
            And there's no doing anything about it!

                              T. S. Eliot

281

Antonio

Antonio, Antonio,
Was tired of living alonio.
    He thought he would woo
    Miss Lissamy Lou,
Miss Lissamy Lucy Molonio.

Antonio, Antonio,
Rode off on his polo-ponio.
    He found the fair maid
    In a bowery shade,
A-sitting and knitting alonio.

Antonio, Antonio,
Said, "If you will be my ownio,
    I'll love you true,
    And I'll buy for you,
An icery creamery conio!"

"Oh, nonio, Antonio!
You're far too bleak and bonio!
    And all that I wish,
    You singular fish,
Is that you will quickly begonio."

Antonio, Antonio,
He uttered a dismal moanio;
    Then ran off and hid
    (Or I'm told that he did)
In the Antarctical Zonio.

Laura E. Richards

House on the Hill

Higgity, biggity,
diggity dill,
a little round house
sits on a high hill.
It sits on the hill
like a hat on a head,
the roof has a peak and
the chimney is red.
And just like a feather
on somebody's hat,
the smoke curls up
as jaunty as that.
At night two windows
are two yellow eyes,
like somebody staring
in mild surprise.

Figgity, tiggity,
wiggity will,
I'll save up my dimes
and my pennies until
I can live on that hill.
Then I'll look down,
out of those windows
over the town.
The smoke will curl
and the windows blink.
Folk will stare
and I shall wink.
O, diggity dill,
that house on the hill,
I can see me there now
at the window sill.

Nora S. Unwin

The Mysterious Cat

GIRLS.	I saw a proud, mysterious cat,
BOYS.	I saw a proud, mysterious cat
SOLO 1.	Too proud to catch a mouse or rat—
ALL.	Mew, mew, mew.

GIRLS.	But catnip she would eat, and purr,
BOYS.	But catnip she would eat, and purr.
SOLO 2.	And goldfish she did much prefer—
ALL.	Mew, mew, mew.

GIRLS.	I saw a cat—'twas but a dream,
BOYS.	I saw a cat—'twas but a dream,
SOLO 3.	Who scorned the slave that brought her cream—
ALL.	Mew, mew, mew.

GIRLS.	Unless the slave were dressed in style,
BOYS.	Unless the slave were dressed in style,
SOLO 4.	And knelt before her all the while—
ALL.	Mew, mew, mew.

GIRLS.	Did you ever hear of a thing like that?
BOYS.	Did you ever hear of a thing like that?
ALL.	Did you ever hear of a thing like that?
GIRLS.	Oh, what a proud, mysterious cat.
BOYS.	Oh, what a proud, mysterious cat.
ALL.	Oh, what a proud, mysterious cat.

Mew . . . Mew . . . Mew.

Vachel Lindsay

Some Poems Tell Stories

Story-poems were first told and sung hundreds of years ago and are still being enjoyed today. They may tell about important events, great heroes, or brave deeds, or about unusual happenings in the lives of everyday people.

Johnny Appleseed

Of Jonathan Chapman
Two things are known:
That he loved apples,
That he walked alone.

At seventy-odd
He was gnarled as could be,
But ruddy and sound
As a good apple tree.

For fifty years over
Of harvest and dew,
He planted his apples
Where no apples grew.

The winds of the prairie
Might blow through his rags,
But he carried his seeds
In the best deerskin bags.

From old Ashtabula
To frontier Fort Wayne,
He planted and pruned
And he planted again.

He had not a hat
To encumber his head.
He wore a tin pan
On his white hair instead.

He nested with owl,
And with bear cub and 'possum,
And knew all his orchards,
Root, tendril, and blossom.

A fine old man,
As ripe as a pippin,
His heart still light,
And his step still skipping.

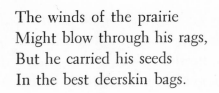

The stalking Indian,
The beast in its lair,
Did no hurt
While he was there;

For they could tell,
As wild things can,
That Jonathan Chapman
Was God's own man.

Why did he do it?
We do not know.
He wished that apples
Might root and grow.

He has no statue.
He has no tomb.
He has his apple trees
Still in bloom.

Consider, consider,
Think well upon
The marvelous story
Of Appleseed John.

Rosemary and
Stephen Vincent Benét

The Raggle, Taggle Gypsies

'Twas late last night when my lord came home,
  Inquiring for his lady, O.
The servants said on every hand,
  "She's gone with the Raggle, Taggle Gypsies, O."

"Oh, saddle for me my milk-white steed,
  Oh, saddle for me my pony, O,
That I may ride and seek my bride
  Who's gone with the Raggle, Taggle Gypsies, O."

Oh, he rode high and he rode low,
  He rode through woods and copses, O,
Until he came to an open field,
  And there he espied his lady, O.

288

"What makes you leave your house and lands?
  What makes you leave your money, O?
What makes you leave your new-wedded lord
  To go with the Raggle, Taggle Gypsies, O?"

"What care I for my house and lands?
  What care I for my money, O?
What care I for my new-wedded lord?
  I'm off with the Raggle, Taggle Gypsies, O."

"Last night you slept on a goose-feather bed,
  With the sheet turned down so bravely, O.
Tonight you will sleep in the cold, open field,
  Along with the Raggle, Taggle Gypsies, O."

"What care I for your goose-feather bed,
  With the sheet turned down so bravely, O?
For tonight I shall sleep in a cold, open field,
  Along with the Raggle, Taggle Gypsies, O."

Old Folk Song

289

The Pirate Don Durk of Dowdee

Ho, for the Pirate Don Durk of Dowdee!
He was as wicked as wicked could be,
But oh, he was perfectly gorgeous to see!
  The Pirate Don Durk of Dowdee.

His conscience, of course, was as black as a bat,
But he had a floppety plume on his hat
And when he went walking it jiggled—like that!
  The plume of the Pirate Dowdee.

His coat it was crimson and cut with a slash,
And often as ever he twirled his mustache
Deep down in the ocean the mermaids went splash,
  Because of Don Durk of Dowdee.

Moreover, Dowdee had a purple tattoo,
And stuck in his belt where he buckled it through
Were a dagger, a dirk and a squizzamaroo,
  For fierce was the Pirate Dowdee.

So fearful he was he would shoot at a puff,
And always at sea when the weather grew rough
He drank from a bottle and wrote on his cuff,
  Did Pirate Don Durk of Dowdee.

Oh, he had a cutlass that swung at his thigh
And he had a parrot called Pepperkin Pye,
And a zigzaggy scar at the end of his eye
  Had Pirate Don Durk of Dowdee.

He kept in a cavern, this buccaneer bold,
A curious chest that was covered with mould,
And all of his pockets were jingly with gold!
  Oh jing! went the gold of Dowdee.

His conscience, of course, it was crook'd like a squash,
But both of his boots made a slickery slosh,
And he went through the world with a wonderful swash,
  Did Pirate Don Durk of Dowdee.

It's true he was wicked as wicked could be,
His sins they outnumbered a hundred and three,
But oh, he was perfectly gorgeous to see,
  The Pirate Don Durk of Dowdee.

Mildred Plew Meigs

Meg Merrilies

Old Meg she was a Gipsy,
    And liv'd upon the Moors:
Her bed it was the brown heath turf,
    And her house was out of doors.

Her apples were swart blackberries,
    Her currants pods o' broom;
Her wine was dew of the wild white rose,
    Her book a churchyard tomb.

Her Brothers were the craggy hills,
    Her Sisters larchen trees—
Alone with her great family
    She liv'd as she did please.

No breakfast had she many a morn,
    No dinner many a noon,
And 'stead of supper she would stare
    Full hard against the Moon.

But every morn of woodbine fresh
   She made her garlanding,
And every night the dark glen Yew
   She wove, and she would sing.

And with her fingers old and brown
   She plaited Mats o' Rushes,
And gave them to the Cottagers
   She met among the Bushes.

Old Meg was brave as Margaret Queen
   And tall as Amazon:
An old red blanket cloak she wore;
   A chip hat had she on.
God rest her aged bones somewhere—
   She died full long agone!

John Keats

293

The poet helps you to see everyday things in a new way.
You may even see some things for the very first time through
the eyes of the poet.

Rain Sizes

Rain comes in various sizes.
Some rain is as small as a mist.
It tickles your face with surprises,
And tingles as if you'd been kissed.

Some rain is the size of a sprinkle
And doesn't put out all the sun.
You can see the drops sparkle and twinkle,
And a rainbow comes out when it's done.

Some rain is as big as a nickel
And comes with a crash and a hiss.
It comes down too heavy to tickle.
It's more like a splash than a kiss.

When it rains the right size and you're wrapped in
Your rainclothes, it's fun out of doors.
But run home before you get trapped in
The big rain that rattles and roars.

John Ciardi

City Lights

Into the endless dark
The lights of the buildings shine,
Row upon twinkling row,
Line upon glistening line.
Up and up they mount
Till the tallest seems to be
The topmost taper set
On a towering Christmas tree.

Rachel Field

It Is Raining

ALL.   It is raining.

TRIO.   Where would you like to be in the rain?
                  Where would you like to be?

GROUP 1.   I'd like to be on a city street,
                  where the rain comes down in a driving sheet,
                  where it wets the houses—roof and wall—
                  the wagons and horses and autos and all.
                  That's where I'd like to be in the rain,
                  that's where I'd like to be.

ALL.   It is raining.

TRIO.   Where would you like to be in the rain?
           Where would you like to be?

GROUP 2.   I'd like to be in a tall tree top,
           where the rain comes dripping, drop, drop, drop,
           around on every side:
           where it wets the farmer, the barn, the pig,
           the cows, the chickens both little and big;
           where it batters and beats on a field of wheat
           and makes the little birds hide.

ALL.   It is raining.

TRIO.   Where would you like to be in the rain?
           Where would you like to be?

GROUP 3.   I'd like to be on a ship at sea,
           where everything's wet as wet can be
           and the waves are rolling high,
           where sailors are pulling the ropes and singing,
           and wind's in the rigging and salt spray's stinging,
           and round us sea gulls cry.
           On a dipping skimming ship at sea—
           that's where I'd like to be in the rain;
           that's where I'd like to be!

Lucy Sprague Mitchell

Dandelions

Over the climbing meadows
Where swallow-shadows float,
These are the small gold buttons
On earth's green, windy coat.

Frances Frost

The Pasture

I'm going out to clean the pasture spring;
I'll only stop to rake the leaves away
(And wait to watch the water clear, I may):
I shan't be gone long.—You come too.

I'm going out to fetch the little calf
That's standing by the mother. It's so young
It totters when she licks it with her tongue.
I shan't be gone long.—You come too.

Robert Frost

Poems Without Rhyme

There are some poems that do not rhyme. You will feel the rhythm moving along in these poems and enjoy the word pictures which they paint for you.

Poem

As the cat
climbed over
the top of

the jamcloset
first the right
forefoot

carefully
then the hind
stepped down

into the pit of
the empty
flowerpot

William Carlos Williams

Storm

You crash over the trees,
you crack the live branch—
the branch is white,
the green crushed,
each leaf is rent like split wood.

You burden the trees
with black drops,
you swirl and crash—
you have broken off a weighted leaf
in the wind,
it is hurled out,
whirls up and sinks,
a green stone.

Hilda Doolittle Aldington

300

Snow-Capped Mountain

Snow-capped mountain, so white, so tall,
The whole sea
Must stand behind you!

Snow-capped mountain, with the wind on your
    forehead,
Do you hold the eagles' nests?

Proud thing,
You shine like a lily,
Yet with a different whiteness;
I should not dare to venture
Up your slippery towers,
For I am thinking you lean too far
Over the edge of the World!

Hilda Conkling

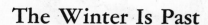

The Winter Is Past

For, lo, the winter is past,
The rain is over and gone;
The flowers appear on the earth;
The time of the singing of birds is come,
And the voice of the turtle is heard in our land.

The Song of Songs

Poems for Special Days

Special days are made for singing. The poet sings about them through the words of a poem. Poems help you to celebrate holidays all the year round.

Columbus

An Italian boy that liked to play
In Genoa about the ships all day,
With curly head and dark, dark eyes,
That gazed at earth in child surprise;
And dreamed of distant stranger skies.

He watched the ships that came crowding in
With cargo of riches; he loved the din
Of the glad rush out and the spreading sails
And the echo of far-off windy gales.

He studied the books of the olden day;
He studied but knew far more than they;
He talked to the learned men of the school—
So wise he was they thought him a fool,
A fool with the dark, dark, dreamful eyes,
A child he was—grown wonder-wise.

Youth and dreams are over past
And out, far out he is sailing fast
Toward the seas he dreamed;—strange lands arise—
The world is made rich by his great emprise—
And the wisest know he was more than wise.

Annette Wynne

I Saw Three Witches

I saw three witches
That bowed down like barley,
And straddled their brooms 'neath a louring sky,
And, mounting a storm-cloud,
Aloft on its margin,
Stood black in the silver as up they did fly.

I saw three witches
That mocked the poor sparrows
They carried in cages of wicker along,
Till a hawk from his eyrie
Swooped down like an arrow,
Smote on the cages, and ended their song.

I saw three witches
That sailed in a shallop,
All turning their heads with a smickering smile,
Till a bank of green osiers
Concealed their wild faces,
Though I heard them lamenting for many a mile.

I saw three witches
Asleep in a valley,
Their heads in a row, like stones in a flood,
Till the moon, creeping upward,
Looked white through the valley,
And turned them to bushes in bright scarlet bud.

Walter de la Mare

Christmas Hearth Rhyme

Sing we all merrily
   Christmas is here,
The day we love best
   Of all days in the year.

Bring forth the holly,
   The box and the bay,
Deck out our cottage
   For glad Christmas day.

Sing we all merrily,
   Draw near the fire,
Sister and brother,
   Grandson and sire.

Old English

My Valentine

I will make you brooches and toys for your delight
Of bird song at morning and starshine at night.
I will make a palace fit for you and me,
   Of green days in forests
   And blue days at sea.

Robert Louis Stevenson

A Valentine

Frost flowers on the window glass,
Hopping chickadees that pass,
Bare old elms that bend and sway,
Pussy willows, soft and gray,

Silver clouds across the sky,
Lacy snowflakes flitting by,
Icicles like fringe in line—
That is Outdoor's valentine!

Eleanor Hammond

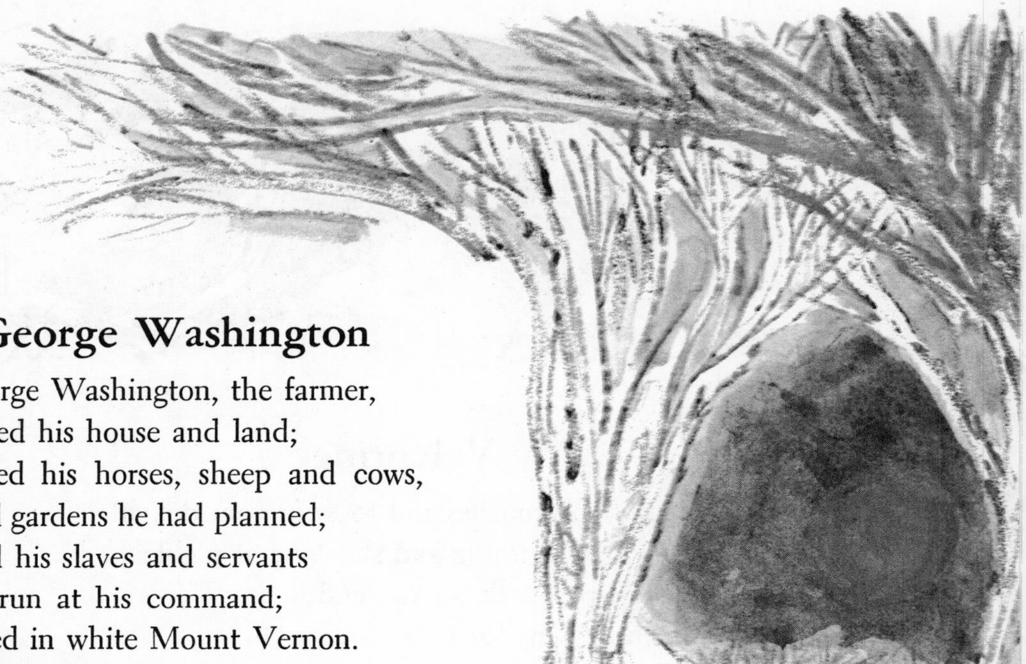

George Washington

George Washington, the farmer,
Loved his house and land;
Loved his horses, sheep and cows,
And gardens he had planned;
Had his slaves and servants
To run at his command;
Lived in white Mount Vernon.
Oh, but he was grand.

George Washington, the fighter,
Knew the Indian's ways;
Led Virginia volunteers
In bloody forest frays.

George Washington, the rebel,
Lived among his men;
Fought the British King's men
Again and yet again;
Slipped across the Delaware;
Grieved at Valley Forge;
Crafty, tender-hearted chief,
Was General George.

Called to serve his country,
As President he came;
Was a man like other men,
Bore his share of blame;
Made his mark upon the world,
An honored, special name;
Helped his country at the start
To do the very same.

And every year upon this day
The land he helped to free
Thinks about George Washington
And makes bold plans to be
In all its Valley Forges
As resolute as he.

James S. Tippett

Written in March

The cock is crowing,
The stream is flowing,
The small birds twitter,
The lake doth glitter,
The green field sleeps in the sun;
The oldest and youngest
Are at work with the strongest;
The cattle are grazing,
Their heads never raising;
There are forty feeding like one!

Like an army defeated
The snow hath retreated,
And now doth fare ill
On the top of the bare hill;
The ploughboy is whooping—anon—anon:
There's joy in the mountains;
There's life in the fountains;
Small clouds are sailing,
Blue sky prevailing;
The rain is over and gone!

William Wordsworth

The Long Story

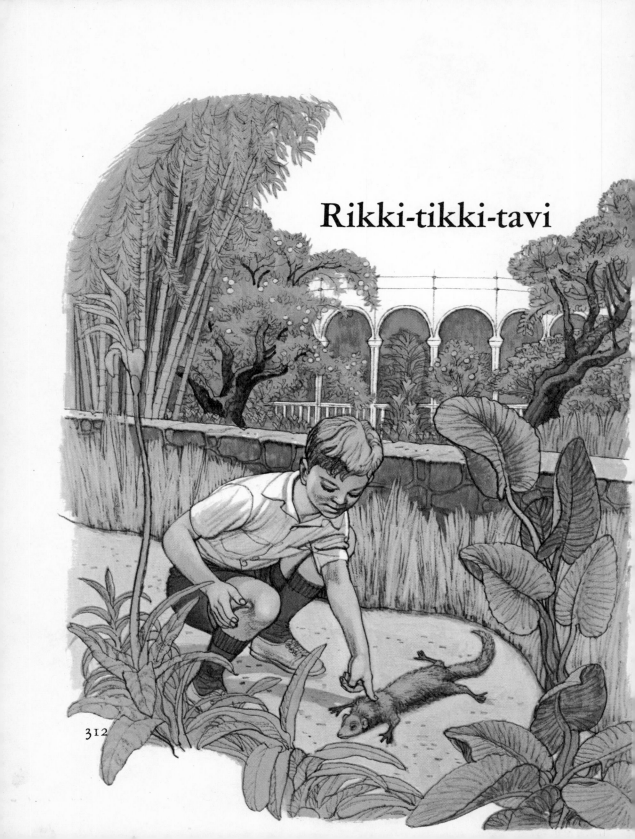

Rikki-tikki-tavi

THIS IS THE STORY of the great war that Rikki-tikki-tavi fought singlehanded, through the bathrooms of the big bungalow in Segowlee cantonment. Darzee, the tailorbird, helped him, and Chuchundra, the muskrat, who never comes out into the middle of the floor, but always creeps round by the wall, gave him advice; but Rikki-tikki did the real fighting.

He was a mongoose, rather like a little cat in his fur and his tail, but quite like a weasel in his head and his habits. His eyes and the end of his restless nose were pink; he could scratch himself anywhere he pleased, with any leg, front or back, that he chose to use; he could fluff up his tail till it looked like a bottle-brush, and his war cry as he scuttled through the long grass was: "*Rikk-tikk-tikki-tikki-tchk!*"

One day a high summer flood washed him out of the burrow where he lived with his father and mother, and carried him, kicking and clucking, down a roadside ditch. He found a little wisp of grass floating there, and clung to it till he lost his senses. When he revived, he was lying in the hot sun on the middle of a garden path, very draggled indeed, and a small boy was saying, "Here's a dead mongoose. Let's have a funeral."

"No," said his mother; "let's take him in and dry him. Perhaps he isn't really dead."

They took him into the house, and a big man picked him up between his finger and thumb and said he was not dead but half choked; so they wrapped him in cotton wool, and warmed him, and he opened his eyes and sneezed.

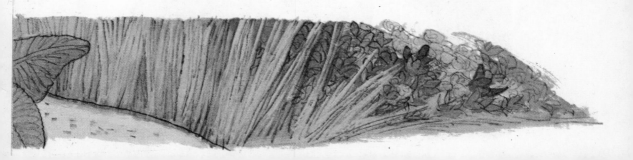

"Now," said the big man (he was an Englishman who had just moved into the bungalow); "don't frighten him, and we'll see what he'll do."

It is the hardest thing in the world to frighten a mongoose, because he is eaten up from nose to tail with curiosity. The motto of all the mongoose family is, "Run and find out"; and Rikki-tikki was a true mongoose. He looked at the cotton wool, decided that it was not good to eat, ran all round the table, sat up and put his fur in order, scratched himself, and jumped on the small boy's shoulder.

"Don't be frightened, Teddy," said his father. "That's his way of making friends."

"Ouch! He's tickling under my chin," said Teddy.

Rikki-tikki looked down between the boy's collar and neck, snuffed at his ear, and climbed down to the floor, where he sat rubbing his nose.

"Good gracious," said Teddy's mother, "and that's a wild creature! I suppose he's so tame because we've been kind to him."

"All mongooses are like that," said her husband. "If Teddy doesn't pick him up by the tail, or try to put him in a cage, he'll run in and out of the house all day long. Let's give him something to eat."

They gave him a little piece of raw meat. Rikki-tikki liked it immensely, and when it was finished he went out into the veranda and sat in the sunshine and fluffed up his fur to make it dry to the roots. Then he felt better.

"There are more things to find out about in this house," he said to himself, "than all my family could find out in all their lives. I shall certainly stay and find out."

He spent all that day roaming over the house. He nearly drowned himself in the bathtubs, put his nose into the ink on a writing table, and burned it on the end of the big man's cigar, for he climbed up in the big man's lap to see how writing was done. At nightfall he ran into Teddy's nursery to watch how kerosene lamps were lighted, and when Teddy went to bed Rikki-tikki climbed up too; but he was a restless companion, because he had to get up and attend to every noise all through the night, and find out what made it. Teddy's mother and father came in, the last thing, to look at their boy, and Rikki-tikki was awake on the pillow. "I don't like that," said Teddy's mother; "he may bite the child."

"He'll do no such thing," said the father. "Teddy's safer with that little beast than if he had a bloodhound to watch him. If a snake came into the nursery now—"

But Teddy's mother wouldn't think of anything so awful.

Early in the morning Rikki-tikki came to early breakfast in the veranda riding on Teddy's shoulder, and they gave him banana and some boiled egg; and he sat on all their laps one after the other, because every well-brought-up mongoose always hopes to be a house-mongoose some day and have rooms to run about in, and Rikki-tikki's mother (she used to live in the General's house at Segowlee) had carefully told Rikki what to do if ever he came across white men.

Then Rikki-tikki went out into the garden to see what was to be seen. It was a large garden, only half cultivated, with bushes as big as summerhouses of Marshal Niel roses, lime and orange trees, clumps of bamboos, and thickets of high grass. Rikki-tikki licked his lips. "This is a splendid hunting ground," he said, and his tail grew bottle-brushy at the thought of it, and he scuttled up and down the garden, snuffing here and there till he heard very sorrowful voices in a thornbush.

It was Darzee, the tailorbird, and his wife. They had made a beautiful nest by pulling two big leaves together and stitching them up the edges with fibers, and had filled the hollow with cotton and downy fluff. The nest swayed to and fro, as they sat on the rim and cried.

"What is the matter?" asked Rikki-tikki.

"We are very miserable," said Darzee. "One of our babies fell out of the nest yesterday and Nag ate him."

"H'm!" said Rikki-tikki, "that is very sad—but I am a stranger here. Who is Nag?"

Darzee and his wife only cowered down in the nest without answering, for from the thick grass at the foot of the bush there came a low hiss—a horrid cold sound that made Rikki-tikki jump back two clear feet. Then inch by inch out of the grass rose up the head and spread hood of Nag, the big black cobra, and he was five feet long from tongue to tail. When he had lifted one-third of himself clear of the ground, he stayed balancing to and fro exactly as a dandelion tuft balances in the wind, and he looked at Rikki-tikki with the wicked snake's eyes that never change their expression, whatever the snake may be thinking of.

317

"Who is Nag?" he said. "*I* am Nag. The great god Brahm put his mark upon all our people when the first cobra spread his hood to keep the sun off Brahm as he slept. Look, and be afraid!"

He spread out his hood more than ever, and Rikki-tikki saw the spectacle mark on the back of it that looks exactly like the eye part of a hook-and-eye fastening. He was afraid for the minute; but it is impossible for a mongoose to stay frightened for any length of time, and though Rikki-tikki had never met a live cobra before, his mother had fed him on dead ones, and he knew that all a grown mongoose's business in life was to fight and eat snakes. Nag knew that too, and at the bottom of his cold heart he was afraid.

"Well," said Rikki-tikki, and his tail began to fluff up again, "marks or no marks, do you think it is right for you to eat fledglings out of a nest?"

Nag was thinking to himself, and watching the least little movement in the grass behind Rikki-tikki. He knew that mongooses in the garden meant death sooner or later for him and his family; but he wanted to get Rikki-tikki off his guard. So he dropped his head a little, and put it on one side.

"Let us talk," he said. "You eat eggs. Why should not I eat birds?"

"Behind you! Look behind you!" sang Darzee.

Rikki-tikki knew better than to waste time in staring. He jumped up in the air as high as he could go, and just under him whizzed by the head of Nagaina, Nag's wicked wife. She had crept up behind him as he was talking, to make an end of him; and he heard her savage hiss as the stroke missed. He came down almost across her back, and if he had been an old mongoose he would have known that then was the time to

break her back with one bite; but he was afraid of the terrible
lashing return-stroke of the cobra. He bit, indeed, but did not
bite long enough, and he jumped clear of the whisking tail,
leaving Nagaina torn and angry.

"Wicked, wicked Darzee!" said Nag, lashing up as high as
he could reach toward the nest in the thornbush; but Darzee
had built it out of reach of snakes, and it only swayed to and
fro.

Rikki-tikki felt his eyes growing red and hot (when a
mongoose's eyes grow red, he is angry), and he sat back on
his tail and hind legs like a little kangaroo, and looked all
around him, and chattered with rage. But Nag and Nagaina
had disappeared into the grass. When a snake misses its stroke,
it never says anything or gives any sign of what it means to
do next. Rikki-tikki did not care to follow them, for he did

not feel sure that he could manage two snakes at once. So he trotted off to the gravel path near the house, and sat down to think. It was a serious matter for him.

If you read the old books of natural history, you will find they say that when the mongoose fights the snake and happens to get bitten, he runs off and eats some herb that cures him. That is not true. The victory is only a matter of quickness of eye and quickness of foot,—snake's blow against mongoose's jump,—and as no eye can follow the motion of a snake's head when it strikes, that makes things much more wonderful than any magic herb. Rikki-tikki knew he was a young mongoose, and it made him all the more pleased to think that he had managed to escape a blow from behind. It gave him confidence in himself, and when Teddy came running down the path, Rikki-tikki was ready to be petted.

But just as Teddy was stooping, something flinched a little in the dust, and a tiny voice said, "Be careful. I am death!" It was Karait, the dusty brown snakeling that lies for choice on the dusty earth; and his bite is as dangerous as the cobra's. But he is so small that nobody thinks of him, and so he does the more harm to people.

Rikki-tikki's eyes grew red again, and he danced up to Karait with the peculiar rocking, swaying motion that he had inherited from his family. It looks very funny, but it is so perfectly balanced a gait that you can fly off from it at any angle you please; and in dealing with snakes this is an advantage. If Rikki-tikki had only known, he was doing a much more dangerous thing than fighting Nag for Karait is so small, and can turn so quickly, that unless Rikki bit him close to the back of the head, he would get the return-stroke in his eye or lip. But Rikki did not know; his eyes were all red, and he rocked back and forth, looking for a good place to hold. Karait struck out. Rikki jumped sideways and tried to run in, but the wicked little dusty gray head lashed within a fraction of his shoulder, and he had to jump over the body, and the head followed his heels close.

Teddy shouted to the house, "Oh, look here! Our mongoose is killing a snake;" and Rikki-tikki heard a scream from Teddy's mother. His father ran out with a stick, but by the time he came up, Karait had lunged out once too far, and Rikki-tikki had sprung, jumped on the snake's back, and dropped his head far between his fore legs, bitten as high up the back as he could get hold, and rolled away. That bite paralyzed Karait, and Rikki-tikki was just going to eat him up from the tail, after the custom of his family at dinner, when he remembered that a full meal makes a slow mongoose, and if he wanted all his strength and quickness ready, he must keep himself thin.

He went away for a dust bath under the castor-oil bushes, while Teddy's father beat the dead Karait. "What is the use of that?" thought Rikki-tikki. "I have settled it all," and then Teddy's mother picked him up from the dust and hugged him, crying that he had saved Teddy from death, and Teddy's father said that he was a providence, and Teddy looked on with big scared eyes. Rikki-tikki was rather amused at all the fuss, which, of course, he did not understand. Teddy's mother might just as well have petted Teddy for playing in the dust. Rikki was thoroughly enjoying himself.

That night, at dinner, walking to and fro among the wine-glasses on the table, he could have stuffed himself three times over with nice things; but he remembered Nag and Nagaina, and though it was very pleasant to be patted and petted by Teddy's mother, and to sit on Teddy's shoulder, his eyes would get red from time to time, and he would go off into his long war cry of *"Rikk-tikk-tikki-tikki-tchk!"*

Teddy carried him off to bed, and insisted on Rikki-tikki sleeping under his chin. Rikki-tikki was too well bred to bite or scratch, but as soon as Teddy was asleep he went off for his nightly walk round the house, and in the dark he ran up against Chuchundra, the muskrat, creeping round by the wall. Chuchundra is a broken-hearted little beast. He whimpers and cheeps all the night, trying to make up his mind to run into the middle of the room, but he never gets there.

"Don't kill me," said Chuchundra, almost weeping. "Rikki-tikki, don't kill me."

"Do you think a snake-killer kills muskrats?" said Rikki-tikki scornfully.

"Those who kill snakes get killed by snakes," said Chuchundra, more sorrowfully than ever. "And how am I to be sure that Nag won't mistake me for you some dark night?"

"There's not the least danger," said Rikki-tikki; "but Nag is in the garden, and I know you don't go there."

"My cousin Chua, the rat, told me—" said Chuchundra, and then he stopped.

"Told you what?"

322

"H'sh! Nag is everywhere, Rikki-tikki. You should have talked to Chua in the garden."

"I didn't—so you must tell me. Quick, Chuchundra, or I'll bite you!"

Chuchundra sat down and cried till the tears rolled off his whiskers. "I am a very poor man," he sobbed. "I never had spirit enough to run out into the middle of the room. H'sh! I mustn't tell you anything. Can't you *hear*, Rikki-tikki?"

Rikki-tikki listened. The house was as still as still, but he thought he could just catch the faintest *scratch-scratch* in the world,—a noise as faint as that of a wasp walking on a window-pane,—the dry scratch of a snake's scales on brickwork.

"That's Nag or Nagaina," he said to himself; "and he is crawling into the bathroom sluice. You're right, Chuchundra; I should have talked to Chua."

He stole off to Teddy's bathroom, but there was nothing there, and then to Teddy's mother's bathroom. At the bottom of the smooth plaster wall there was a brick pulled out to make a sluice for the bath water, and as Rikki-tikki stole in by the masonry curb where the bath is put, he heard Nag and Nagaina whispering together outside in the moonlight.

"When the house is emptied of people," said Nagaina to her husband, "*he* will have to go away, and then the garden will be our own again. Go in quietly, and remember that the big man who killed Karait is the first one to bite. Then come out and tell me, and we will hunt for Rikki-tikki together."

"But are you sure that there is anything to be gained by killing the people?" said Nag.

"Everything. When there were no people in the bungalow, did we have any mongoose in the garden? So long as the bungalow is empty, we are king and queen of the garden; and remember that as soon as our eggs in the melon bed hatch (as they may tomorrow), our children will need room and quiet."

"I had not thought of that," said Nag. "I will go, but there is no need that we should hunt for Rikki-tikki afterward. I will kill the big man and his wife, and the child if I can, and come away quietly. Then the bungalow will be empty, and Rikki-tikki will go."

Rikki-tikki tingled all over with rage and hatred at this, and then Nag's head came through the sluice, and his five feet of cold body followed it. Angry as he was, Rikki-tikki was very frightened as he saw the size of the big cobra. Nag coiled himself up, raised his head, and looked into the bathroom in the dark, and Rikki could see his eyes glitter.

"Now, if I kill him here, Nagaina will know; and if I fight him on the open floor, the odds are in his favor. What am I to do?" said Rikki-tikki-tavi.

Nag waved to and fro, and then Rikki-tikki heard him drinking from the biggest water jar that was used to fill the bath. "That is good," said the snake. "Now, when Karait was killed, the big man had a stick. He may have that stick still, but when he comes in to bathe in the morning he will not have a stick. I shall wait here till he comes. Nagaina—do you hear me?—I shall wait here in the cool till daytime."

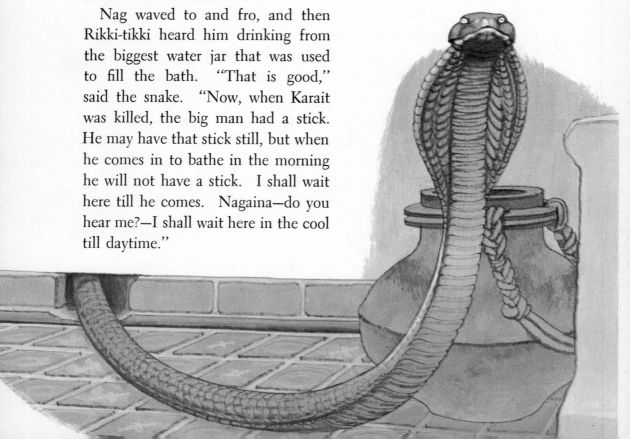

There was no answer from outside, so Rikki-tikki knew Nagaina had gone away. Nag coiled himself down, coil by coil, round the bulge at the bottom of the water jar, and Rikki-tikki stayed still as death. After an hour he began to move, muscle by muscle, toward the jar. Nag was asleep, and Rikki-tikki looked at his big back, wondering which would be the best place for a good hold. "If I don't break his back at the first jump," said Rikki, "he can still fight; and if he fights—O Rikki!" He looked at the thickness of the neck below the hood, but that was too much for him; and a bite near the tail would only make Nag savage.

"It must be the head," he said at last; "the head above the hood; and, when I am once there, I must not let go."

Then he jumped. The head was lying a little clear of the water jar, under the curve of it; and, as his teeth met, Rikki braced his back against the bulge of the red earthenware to hold down the head. This gave him just one second's purchase, and he made the most of it. Then he was battered to and fro as a rat is shaken by a dog—to and fro on the floor, up and down, and round in great circles; but his eyes were red, and he held on as the body cartwhipped over the floor, upsetting the tin dipper and the soap dish and the fleshbrush, and banged against the tin side of the bath. As he held he closed his jaws tighter and tighter, for he made sure he would be banged to death, and, for the honor of his family, he preferred to be

325

found with his teeth locked. He was dizzy, aching, and felt shaken to pieces when something went off like a thunderclap just behind him; a hot wind knocked him senseless and red fire singed his fur. The big man had been wakened by the noise, and had fired both barrels of a shotgun into Nag just behind the hood.

Rikki-tikki held on with his eyes shut, for now he was quite sure he was dead; but the head did not move, and the big man picked him up and said, "It's the mongoose again, Alice; the little chap has saved *our* lives now." Then Teddy's mother came in with a very white face, and saw what was left of Nag, and Rikki-tikki dragged himself to Teddy's bedroom and spent half the rest of the night shaking himself tenderly to find out whether he really was broken into forty pieces, as he fancied.

When morning came he was very stiff, but well pleased with his doings. "Now I have Nagaina to settle with, and she will be worse than five Nags, and there's no knowing when the eggs she spoke of will hatch. Goodness! I must go and see Darzee," he said.

Without waiting for breakfast, Rikki-tikki ran to the thornbush where Darzee was singing a song of triumph at the top of his voice. The news of Nag's death was all over the garden, for the sweeper had thrown the body on the rubbish heap.

"Oh, you stupid tuft of feathers!" said Rikki-tikki, angrily. "Is this the time to sing?"

"Nag is dead—is dead—is dead!" sang Darzee. "The valiant Rikki-tikki caught him by the head and held fast. The big man brought the bang-stick and Nag fell in two pieces! He will never eat my babies again."

"All that's true enough; but where's Nagaina?" said Rikki-tikki, looking carefully round him.

"Nagaina came to the bathroom sluice and called for Nag," Darzee went on; "and Nag came out on the end of a stick—the sweeper picked him up on the end of a stick and threw him upon the rubbish heap. Let us sing about the great, the red-eyed Rikki-tikki!" and Darzee filled his throat and sang.

"If I could get up to your nest, I'd roll all your babies out!" said Rikki-tikki. "You don't know when to do the right thing at the right time. You're safe enough in your nest there, but it's war for me down here. Stop singing a minute, Darzee."

"For the great, the beautiful Rikki-tikki's sake I will stop," said Darzee. "What is it, O Killer of the terrible Nag?"

"Where is Nagaina, for the third time?"

"On the rubbish heap by the stables, mourning for Nag. Great is Rikki-tikki with the white teeth."

"Bother my white teeth! Have you ever heard where she keeps her eggs?"

"In the melon bed, on the end nearest the wall, where the sun strikes nearly all day. She had them there weeks ago."

"And you never thought it worth while to tell me? The end nearest the wall, you said?"

"Rikki-tikki, you are not going to eat her eggs?"

"Not eat exactly; no. Darzee, if you have a grain of sense you will fly off to the stables and pretend that your wing is broken, and let Nagaina chase you away to this bush! I must get to the melon bed, and if I went there now she'd see me."

Darzee was a feather-brained little fellow who could never hold more than one idea at a time in his head; and just because he knew that Nagaina's children were born in eggs like his own, he didn't think at first that it was fair to kill them. But his wife was a sensible bird, and she knew that cobra's eggs meant young cobras later on; so she flew off from the nest, and left Darzee to keep the babies warm, and continue his song about the death of Nag. Darzee was very like a man in some ways.

She fluttered in front of Nagaina by the rubbish heap, and cried out, "Oh, my wing is broken! The boy in the house threw a stone at me and broke it." Then she fluttered more desperately than ever.

Nagaina lifted up her head and hissed, "You warned Rikki-tikki when I would have killed him. Indeed and truly, you've chosen a bad place to be lame in." And she moved toward Darzee's wife, slipping along over the dust.

"The boy broke it with a stone!" shrieked Darzee's wife.

"Well! It may be some consolation to you when you're dead to know that I shall settle accounts with the boy. My husband lies on the rubbish heap this morning, but before night the boy in the house will lie very still. What is the use of running away? I am sure to catch you. Little fool, look at me!"

Darzee's wife knew better than to do *that*, for a bird who looks at a snake's eyes gets so frightened that she cannot move. Darzee's wife fluttered on, piping sorrowfully, and never leaving the ground, and Nagaina quickened her pace.

Rikki-tikki heard them going up the path from the stables, and he raced for the end of the melon patch near the wall. There, in the warm litter about the melons, very cunningly hidden, he found twenty-five eggs, about the size of a bantam's eggs, but with whitish skin instead of shell.

"I was not a day too soon," he said; for he could see the baby cobras curled up inside the skin, and he knew that the minute they were hatched they could each kill a man or a mongoose. He bit off the tops of the eggs as fast as he could, taking care to crush the young cobras, and turned over the litter from time to time to see whether he had missed any. At last there were only three eggs left, and Rikki-tikki began to chuckle to himself, when he heard Darzee's wife screaming:

"Rikki-tikki, I led Nagaina toward the house, and she has gone into the veranda, and—oh, come quickly—she means killing!"

Rikki-tikki smashed two eggs, and tumbled backward down the melon bed with the third egg in his mouth, and scuttled to the veranda as hard as he could put foot to the ground. Teddy and his mother and father were there at early breakfast; but Rikki-tikki saw that they were not eating anything. They sat stone-still, and their faces were white. Nagaina was coiled up on the matting by Teddy's chair, within easy striking distance of Teddy's bare leg, and she was swaying to and fro singing a song of triumph.

"Son of the big man that killed Nag," she hissed, "stay still. I am not ready yet. Wait a little. Keep very still, all you three. If you move I strike, and if you do not move I strike. Oh, foolish people, who killed my Nag!"

Teddy's eyes were fixed on his father, and all his father could do was to whisper, "Sit still, Teddy. You mustn't move. Teddy, keep still."

Then Rikki-tikki came up and cried, "Turn round, Nagaina; turn and fight!"

"All in good time," said she, without moving her eyes. "I will settle my account with *you* presently. Look at your friends, Rikki-tikki. They are still and white; they are afraid. They dare not move, and if you come a step nearer I strike."

330

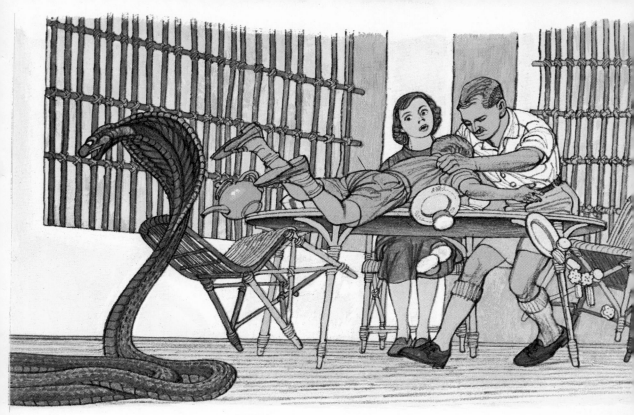

"Look at your eggs," said Rikki-tikki, "in the melon bed near the wall. Go and look, Nagaina."

The big snake turned half round, and saw the egg on the veranda. "Ah-h! Give it to me," she said.

Rikki-tikki put his paws one on each side of the egg, and his eyes were blood-red. "What price for a snake's egg? For a young cobra? For a young king cobra? For the last—the very last of the brood? The ants are eating all the others down by the melon bed."

Nagaina spun clear round, forgetting everything for the sake of the one egg; and Rikki-tikki saw Teddy's father shoot out a big hand, catch Teddy by the shoulder and drag him across the little table with the teacups, safe and out of reach of Nagaina.

"Tricked! Tricked! Tricked! *Rikk-tck-tck!*" chuckled Rikki-tikki. "The boy is safe, and it was I—I—I that caught Nag by the hood last night in the bathroom." Then he began to jump up and down, all four feet together, his head close to the floor. "He threw me to and fro, but he could not shake me off. He was dead before the big man blew him in two. I did it. *Rikki-tikki-tck-tck!* Come then, Nagaina. Come and fight with me. You shall not be a widow long."

Nagaina saw that she had lost her chance of killing Teddy, and the egg lay between Rikki-tikki's paws. "Give me the egg, Rikki-tikki. Give me the last of my eggs, and I will go away and never come back," she said, lowering her hood.

"Yes, you will go away, and you will never come back; for you will go to the rubbish heap with Nag. Fight, widow! The big man has gone for his gun! Fight!"

Rikki-tikki was bounding all round Nagaina, keeping just out of the reach of her stroke, his little eyes like hot coals. Nagaina gathered herself together, and flung out at him. Rikki-tikki jumped up and backward. Again and again and again she struck, and each time her head came with a whack on the matting of the veranda and she gathered herself together like a watch spring. Then Rikki-tikki danced in a circle to get behind her, and Nagaina spun round to keep her head to his head, so that the rustle of her tail on the matting sounded like dry leaves blown along by the wind.

He had forgotten the egg. It still lay on the veranda, and Nagaina came nearer and nearer to it, till at last, while Rikki-tikki was drawing breath, she caught it in her mouth, turned to the veranda steps, and flew like an arrow down the path, with Rikki-tikki behind her. When the cobra runs for her life, she goes like a whiplash flicked across a horse's neck.

Rikki-tikki knew that he must catch her, or all the trouble would begin again. She headed straight for the long grass by the thornbush, and as he was running Rikki-tikki heard Darzee still singing his foolish little song of triumph. But Darzee's wife was wiser. She flew off her nest as Nagaina came along, and flapped her wings about Nagaina's head. If Darzee had helped they might have turned her; but Nagaina only lowered her hood and went on. Still, the instant's delay brought Rikki-tikki up to her, and as she plunged into the rathole where she and Nag used to live, his little white teeth were clenched on her tail, and he went down with her—and very few mongooses, however wise and old they may be, care to follow a cobra into its hole. It was dark in the hole; and Rikki-tikki never knew when it might open out and give Nagaina room to turn and strike at him. He held on savagely, and struck out his feet to act as brakes on the dark slope of the hot, moist earth.

333

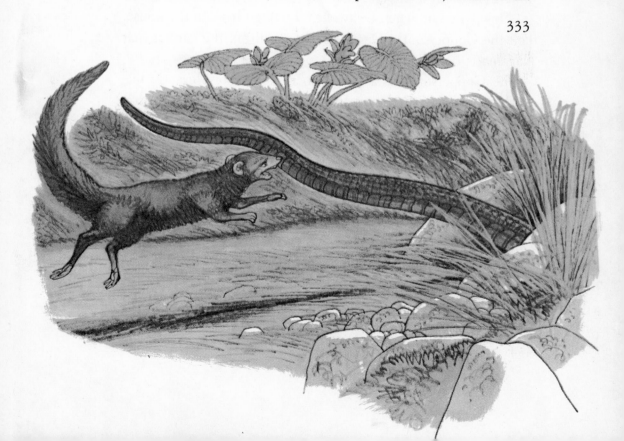

Then the grass by the mouth of the hole stopped waving, and Darzee said, "It is all over with Rikki-tikki! We must sing his death-song. Valiant Rikki-tikki is dead! For Nagaina will surely kill him underground."

So he sang a very mournful song that he made up all on the spur of the minute, and just as he got to the most touching part the grass quivered again, and Rikki-tikki, covered with dirt, dragged himself out of the hole leg by leg, licking his whiskers. Darzee stopped with a little shout. Rikki-tikki shook some of the dust out of his fur and sneezed. "It is all over," he said. "The widow will never come out again." And the red ants that live between the grass stems heard him, and began to troop down one after another to see if he had spoken the truth.

Rikki-tikki curled himself up in the grass and slept where he was—slept and slept till it was late in the afternoon, for he had done a hard day's work.

"Now," he said when he awoke, "I will go back to the house. Tell the Coppersmith, Darzee, and he will tell the garden that Nagaina is dead."

The Coppersmith is a bird who makes a noise exactly like the beating of a little hammer on a copper pot; and the reason he is always making it is because he is the town crier to every Indian garden, and tells all the news to everybody who cares to listen. As Rikki-tikki went up the path, he heard his "attention" notes like a tiny dinner gong; and then the steady "*Ding-dong-tock! Nag is dead—dong! Nagaina is dead! Ding-dong-tock!*" That set all the birds in the garden singing, and the frogs croaking; for Nag and Nagaina used to eat frogs as well as little birds.

When Rikki got to the house, Teddy and Teddy's mother (she looked very white still, for she had been fainting) and

Teddy's father came out and almost cried over him; and that night he ate all that was given him till he could eat no more, and went to bed on Teddy's shoulder, where Teddy's mother saw him when she came to look late at night.

"He saved our lives and Teddy's life," she said to her husband. "Just think, he saved all our lives."

Rikki-tikki woke up with a jump, for all the mongooses are light sleepers.

"Oh, it's you," said he. "What are you bothering for? All the cobras are dead; and if they weren't, I'm here."

Rikki-tikki had a right to be proud of himself; but he did not grow too proud, and he kept that garden as a mongoose should keep it, with tooth and jump and spring and bite, till never a cobra dared show its head inside the walls.

Rudyard Kipling

Learning More About the Story

Rudyard Kipling was an Englishman who spent part of his life in India, where he gathered many ideas for his writing. The scene of the story "Rikki-tikki-tavi" is the cantonment at Segowlee, a small town in northeast India. What clues can you find which suggest that the story takes place in India?

The story was written in 1894 when India was still part of the British Empire. What clues can you find which suggest that the story happened more than half a century ago?

Describe the garden around the bungalow. Compare the trees, plants, birds, and animals with those in your neighborhood. Make one list of the things that are alike and another of those that are different.

This story begins with the high summer flood. Why is this event important? How does the killing of Nag help to advance the action of the plot? What is the climax of the story? What happens after the climax?

The main character in the story is Rikki-tikki-tavi. Why is he so important? What words would you use to describe him? How did each of the following characters feel about Rikki: Teddy, Nagaina, Darzee, Teddy's mother?

Darzee is described as a feather-brained fellow who didn't know how to do the right thing at the right time. What evidence from the story can you give to prove that this is true?

The author's style of making animals talk with wit and wisdom holds the interest of the reader. What are some of the things the animals say that make them seem human?

Vivid comparisons called similes give added meaning and enjoyment to the story. Each of the following questions contains a simile from the story. Tell to whom each refers.

What made "a noise as faint as that of a wasp walking
on a window pane"?

Whose tail "looked like a bottle-brush"?

Who ran "like a whiplash flicked across a horse's
neck"?

Who made a noise "like the beating of a little hammer on a copper pot"?

Whose tail rustling on the matting "sounded like
dry leaves blown along by the wind"?

Thinking About the Story

Read aloud the paragraph at the beginning of the story which
describes the mongoose. Why is it difficult to frighten a
mongoose? Give the motto of the mongoose family. What is
this animal's "business in life"? Why is he able to fight and
kill snakes? Why was it so dangerous for Rikki-tikki to fight
Karait?

What did Teddy's father mean when he said, "Teddy is
safer with that little beast than if he had a bloodhound to
watch him"?

How did Rikki-tikki happen to hear Nag and Nagaina
making plans? What were they going to do? How did
Rikki-tikki prevent these plans from being carried out?

After Nag was killed, Rikki-tikki still had to face something
worse than five Nags. What was it? Why was Darzee's wife
such a big help to Rikki-tikki? How did Rikki trick Nagaina
and again save Teddy's life? What did Rikki-tikki finally do
that very few mongooses dare to do?

Why did Rikki-tikki have a right to be proud of himself?
Discuss your reasons. Why do you think Rikki-tikki-tavi was
an appropriate name?

Some Books to Read

Alphonse, That Bearded One, by Natalie Savage Carlson.
A tall tale about a bear that, trained to shoulder a gun, was sent to fight the Iroquois in place of his master.

Balboa: Finder of the Pacific, by Ronald Syme.
Good maps and attractive illustrations add interest to this exciting story of a great explorer.

Benjamin Franklin, by Ingri and Edgar Parin d'Aulaire.
A lively account with lovely pictures of one of America's most colorful ancestors.

Beyond the High Hills, A Book of Eskimo Poems.
An unusual collection of poems describing Eskimo life in the Hudson Bay region. Excellent photographs depict the mood of each poem.

Bubo, The Great Horned Owl, by John L. and Jean C. George.
Exciting adventures of Bubo, his mate, and other forest creatures.

Castaways in Lilliput, by Henry Winterfield.
Three children drift in a rubber raft to a strange country where they experience their own "Gulliver's Travels."

The Children of Green Knowe, by Lucy M. Boston.
Tolly found playmates from an earlier century when he visited his great-grandmother's old castle.

Kildee House, by Rutherford Montgomery.
When Jerome Kildee built his home in a redwood tree, he didn't know he would be sharing it with a family of skunks and one of the raccoons.

Norwegian Folk Tales, by Peter C. Asbjornsen and Jorgen Moe.
A new translation of a group of famous folk tales.

The Terrible Churnadryne, by Eleanore Cameron.
Mystery and adventure along a fog-bound coast greet Tom and Jennifer when they try to solve the secret of the "monster."

What Then, Raman?, by Shirley Lease Arora.
A village boy in India discovers the excitement of learning and the importance of sharing his knowledge.

Your Glossary

This glossary will help you to pronounce and to understand the meanings of the more difficult words in this book. A number after the definition of a word indicates the first page on which the word, or some form of the word, is used with that particular meaning.

Below is a list of pronunciation symbols and of words that tell you the sounds for which the symbols stand. It is called a pronunciation key.

ā	lāte	ē	wē	ō	ōld	o͞o	mo͞on
ȧ	al′wȧys	ê	ê nough′	ȯ	ȯ bey′	o͝o	fo͝ot
ă	ăm	ĕ	wĕt	ŏ	nŏt	oi	oil
ă	ăp pear′	ĕ	si′lĕnt	ŏ	cŏn trol′	ou	out
ä	färm	ẽ	let′tẽr	ô	hôrse	th	that
ȧ	ȧsk	ḙ	hḙre	ð	sȯft	th	thin
à	à lone′	ī	hīde	ū	ūse	tû	na′tûre
â	câre	ĭ	hĭd	û	û nite′		
		ĭ	pos′sĭ ble	ŭ	ŭs		
				ŭ	cir′cŭs		
				û	bûrn		

A

a ca′cia (ȧ kā′shȧ). A woody shrub or tree that grows in warm climates. It bears small yellow or white flowers growing in clusters. (130)

Acacia.

Ach met′ (äk mĕt′). The head groom in the story "King of the Wind." (136)

Ag′ba (äg′bȧ). The boy who took care of horses in the story "King of the Wind." (136)

Ak′ka (äk′ȧ). A wise goose who was leader of the wild geese in the story "The Wonderful Adventure of Nils." (184)

Al′lah (ăl′ȧ). The Supreme Being of the Mohammedans. (142)

al′ter nate (ôl′tẽr nĭt), *adj.* 1. Every other; every second one; as, the *alternate* lines of a poem. (160) 2. Occurring by turns, first one and then the other; as, *alternate* sunshine and showers.

al′ter nate (ôl′tẽr nāt), *v.* To take turns; as, to *alternate* in doing the dishes.

André Garnerin. See Garnerin, André.

an tic′i pa′tion (ăn tĭs′ĭ pā′shŭn). A looking forward to; expectation. (80)

a pol′o gy (ȧ pŏl′ȯ jĭ). An expression of regret for something one has done. (73)

As′gard (äs′gärd). In Norse mythology, the home of the gods, reached only by the bridge Bifrost. (240)

339

av′a lanche (ăv′*à* lànch). 1. A sudden great, or overwhelming descent of anything. (56) 2. A large mass of snow and ice, or of earth and rock, sliding down a mountainside or over a steep cliff.

a venge′ (*à* vĕnj′). 1. To get satisfaction for; to get revenge for. (234) 2. To give just punishment for a crime or a wrong done to a person.

az′ure (ăzh′ẽr). The blue color of the clear sky. (271)

B

Bag′dad or **Bagh′dad** (băg′dăd). The capital of Iraq, a country in southwestern Asia. (261)

ban′ter (băn′tẽr). 1. Good-humored or playful joking and teasing. (191) 2. To make fun of in a good-humored way.

Be′o wulf (bā′ŏ wŏŏlf). The Anglo-Saxon warrior hero in the story "Beowulf's Fight with Grendel." (226)

Ber nard′ de Men′ thon′ (bẽr närd′ dĕ män′ tôn′). A holy man who established the Hospice of Saint Bernard situated at the top of Great St. Bernard Pass. (36)

be witch′ (bĕ wĭch′). 1. To cast a spell over; to put under a spell; to gain an influence over a person by means of magic or charms. (190) 2. To attract greatly; to fascinate.

bil′low (bĭl′ō). 1. To bulge or swell out. (48) 2. To roll in great waves; as, the *billowing* sea.

bog (bŏg). Wet, spongy ground; a marsh; a swamp. (234)

bois′ter ous (bois′tẽr ŭs). 1. Rough and noisy; as, a *boisterous* crowd. (67) 2. Stormy; violent; as, a *boisterous* wind.

brace (brās). 1. To make strong, firm, or steady; to hold or fix firmly in place. (115) 2. That which supports something firmly; as, a *brace* for a sagging door. 3. A pair; a couple; as, a *brace* of ducks.

Brahm (bräm). In the Hindu religion, the god who created the world. (318)

bram′ble (brăm′b'l). A prickly shrub, such as a raspberry or blackberry bush. (73)

Bramble.

bran′dish (brăn′dĭsh). To wave or shake in a threatening way; as, to *brandish* a sword. (70)

breech′clout′ (brēch′klout′). A cloth worn around the lower part of the body. (69)

breed (brēd). 1. A kind or variety of animal or plant. (42) 2. To raise, as dogs or horses, for sale or to develop improved forms. 3. To give birth to.

bridge (brĭj). In broadcasting, a short passage of music or sound effects connecting two acts of a play, or two parts of a program. (251)

bris′tle (brĭs′'l). 1. A short, stiff hair, as on the back of a pig. (245) 2. One of the stiff hairs, or something like a hair, on a brush. 3. To rise or stand up like the bristles of a hog. 4. To show anger.

Brok (brŏk). The name of a dwarf in the Norse myth "The Making of the Hammer." (243)

browse (brouz). 1. To nibble on grass or leaves; to graze. (112) 2. To read here and there in a book or in a library.

buck'ler (bŭk'lẽr). A small round shield worn on the arm and used to protect the front part of the body. (229)

Buckler.

Bu'da pest' (boō'dȧ pĕst'). The capital of Hungary, formerly the two cities of Buda and Pest, one on either side of the Danube River. (44)

bur'nish (bûr'nĭsh). To make shiny, especially by rubbing; to polish. (271)

buz'zard (bŭz'ẽrd). 1. Any of several heavy short-winged hawks, rather slow in flight. (186) 2. A kind of vulture that feeds on the dead bodies of animals.

C

Cae'sar (sē'zẽr). A famous Roman general and statesman of olden times. (38)

can ton'ment (kăn tŏn'mĕnt). 1. In India, a military post. (313) 2. A group of temporary structures for housing troops.

cap size' (kăp sīz'). To upset or overturn. (57)

car'a way (kăr'ȧ wā). A plant of the carrot family bearing flattish white flower heads and fragrant, spicy seeds which are used in cooking. (186)

cart'whip' (kärt'hwĭp'). To lash about in moving folds like a cart whip which is a heavy whip. (325)

Chan'ti cleer (chăn'tĭ klēr). 1. The name of the rooster in the story "Chanticleer and the Fox." (270) 2. A rooster.

chap'ar ral' (shăp'ȧ răl'). A thicket of dwarf evergreen oaks; also, any dense thicket of stiff or thorny shrubs or dwarf trees. (30)

chore (chōr). A small task or odd job. In the *plural*, the regular light work about a house or a farm. (158)

clar'i fy (klăr'ĭ fī). To make clear; to explain; to understand. (100)

clois'ter (klois'tẽr). 1. A quiet place shut away. (185) 2. A covered walk, one side of which is walled. 3. A convent or monastery.

Cloister.

coax (kōks). 1. To persuade, or to try to persuade, by gentle but constant asking. (191) 2. To influence by pleasant talk and ways.

co'bra (kō'brȧ). A very poisonous snake of Asia and Africa. When excited, it puffs out the skin around its neck into a hood. (317)

con temp'tu ous ly (kŏn tĕmp'tụ ŭs lĭ). In a way that shows contempt, scorn, or disgust; scornfully. (198)

coun'ci lor (koun'sĭ lẽr). A member of a council; one of an official body of advisers or lawmakers. (250)

---

lāte, alwãys, ăm, ȧppear, färm, ȧsk, ȧlone, câre, wē, ēnough, wĕt, silĕnt, lettẽr, hēre, hīde, hĭd, possĭble, ōld, ȯbey, nŏt, cŏntrol, hôrse, sŏft, ūse, ûnite, ŭs, circŭs, bûrn, moōn, foŏt, oil, out, ~~that~~, thin, natụre

341

cow′er (kou′ẽr). To crouch or shrink with fear. (317)

cro chet′ (krổ shā′). To knit with a single needle having a hook at one end. (158)

cul′ti vate (kŭl′tĭ vāt). 1. To prepare land for the raising of crops; to till the soil. (316) 2. To improve; to develop; as, to *cultivate* the mind.

cun′ning (kŭn′ĭng). 1. Sly; tricky; as, a *cunning* thief. (212) 2. Prettily pleasing or attractive; as, a *cunning* baby.

D

Dan′ube (dăn′ūb). A river flowing from Germany through central Europe into the Black Sea. (45)

daze (dāz). 1. To bewilder or confuse, as with fear or grief; to dazzle with too much light; to stun by a sudden blow. (57) 2. A confused state of mind; as, to be in a *daze*.

deb′o nair′ (dĕb′ổ nâr′). Pleasant and courteous; gay and graceful. (271)

de ceive′ (dĕ sēv′). To cause to believe what is false; to mislead. (215)

De me′ter (dĕ mē′tẽr). In Greek mythology, the goddess of the fruitful soil and of agriculture. (220)

dem′oi selle′ (dĕm′wä zĕl′). A young lady; a damsel. (271)

des′ti na′tion (dĕs′tĭ nā′shŭn). The place set for the end of a journey; the place to which a person or thing is going. (126)

de vour′ (dĕ vour′). 1. To swallow or eat up in a greedy way. (96) 2. To take in eagerly by the eyes or mind; as, to *devour* a story. 3. To destroy,

lay waste; as, the flames *devoured* the building.

di lute′ (dĭ lūt′). 1. To diminish the strength or brilliancy of. (47) 2. To make thinner or weaker by mixing with something else, as with water.

dis creet′ (dĭs krēt′). Having or showing good judgment in speech and conduct. (271)

dis tend′ (dĭs tĕnd′). To stretch out: to swell; to expand. (138)

dor′mouse′ (dôr′mous′). An animal of Europe that looks somewhat like a small squirrel. (194)

Dormouse.

do′ry (dō′rĭ). A flat-bottomed boat with a sharp bow, and with sides that curve upward and outward. (54)

dun′geon (dŭn′jŭn). A close, dark prison, usually underground. (48)

E

earth′en ware′ (ûr′thĕn wâr′). Pottery or ornaments made of clay. (325)

e lude′ (ĕ lūd′). To avoid by being quick or clever; to escape. (82)

e nu′mer ate (ĕ nū′mẽr āt). To count over or name over; to name one by one. (186)

es′ti mate (ĕs′tĭ māt). 1. To figure approximately; to judge; as, to *estimate* the price of a house. (45)

Eu ryd′i ce (ũ rĭd′ĭ sē). In Greek mythology, the young wife of Orpheus. (218)

ex tinct′ (ĕks tĭngkt′). 1. Having no living members; no longer existing. (107) 2. No longer active; as, an *extinct* volcano.

F

fade (fād). In broadcasting, to gradually lessen or diminish the volume of sound. (251)

fal'con (fôl'kŭn). 1. Any one of several long-winged, swift-flying, small hawks. (186) 2. Certain types of hawks trained for hunting birds and small game.

fen (fĕn). Low swampy land; an area of soft, wet land; marsh. (226)

fi'ber (fī'bĕr). 1. A threadlike part of a tough substance or tissue, such as raw wool or cotton. (317) 2. A tough substance or tissue made up of threadlike parts; as, nerve *fiber*.

fledg'ling (flĕj'lĭng). 1. A bird that has just grown the feathers needed for flying. (318) 2. A person who has not yet arrived at full development.

fleece (flēs). 1. The coat of wool that covers a sheep or similar animal. (119) 2. To shear; as, to *fleece* a sheep. 3. To cheat; as, to *fleece* a person of his money.

flim'sy (flĭm'zĭ). Not strong or solid; limp; weak; frail. (69)

foal (fōl). 1. To give birth to. (139) 2. The young of an animal of the horse family; a colt; a filly.

for'age (fŏr'ĭj). 1. Food for horses, cattle, and other animals. (116) 2. To wander about looking for food.

Frey'a (frā'ä). In Norse mythology, the goddess of love and beauty, and the wife of Odin. (246)

G

gad'fly' (găd'flī'). A fly that bites; especially one that stings horses and cattle; a horsefly. (245)

gait (gāt). Manner of walking or running; as, a fast *gait*. (320)

Gar ne rin', An dré' (gàr nĕ răn', än drā'). The first man to jump from a balloon by parachute. (44)

gar'ri son (găr'ĭ sŭn). 1. A fortified place in which troops are regularly stationed. (65) 2. A body of troops stationed in a fort.

ges'ture (jĕs'tŭr). 1. A motion of the body or limbs intended to express a feeling or an idea. (115) 2. To make a motion of the body or limbs to express a feeling or an idea.

Go dol'phin (gŏ dŏl'fĭn). An Arabian horse who founded a line of thoroughbreds. (145)

Gren'del (grĕn'dĕl). The monster slain by Beowulf in the story "Beowulf's Fight with Grendel." (226)

guin'ea fowl (gĭn'ĭ foul). A farm and game bird, having dark-colored plumage sprinkled with white. (131)

Guinea Fowl.

gulch (gŭlch). A deep, steep ravine or gorge; especially, the sharply hollowed bed of a torrent. (28)

Gung'ner (gŏong'nĕr). In Norse mythology, the name of a wonderful spear that never missed its mark. (243)

---

lāte, alwãys, ăm, ăppear, färm, åsk, ȧlone, câre, wē, ênough, wĕt, silĕnt, lettẽr, hẽre, hīde, hĭd, possĭble, ōld, ȯbey, nŏt, cŏntrol, hôrse, sŏft, ūse, ûnite, ŭs, circŭs, bûrn, mōōn, fŏŏt, oil, out, that, thin, natụre

H

Ha′des (hā′dēz). 1. In Greek mythology the god of the lower world. He was also called Pluto. (220) 2. The abode of the dead.

Ham′ e lin (hăm′lĭn) 1. The name of a small town in the story "The Pied Piper." (251) 2. A city in West Germany located on the Weser River.

Han′ni bal (hăn′ĭ băl). A general of ancient Carthage who fought against Rome. (38)

haunch′es (hônch′ĕz). 1. Leg and loin of an animal. (112) 2. The back part of the body where the hips and thighs join; hindquarters.

haunt (hônt). 1. In common use, a ghost. (80) 2. A place visited again and again. 3. To visit repeatedly, as a ghost or spirit; as, to *haunt* a house.

hem′lock (hĕm′lŏk). 1. An evergreen tree of the pine family, or its wood. (105) 2. A poisonous plant.

hemp (hĕmp). A tall plant of Asia whose tough fibers are used for making cloth, floor coverings, and rope. (139)

hind′quar′ters (hīnd′kwôr′tẽrz). The back part of the body of an animal. (116)

hos′pice (hŏs′pĭs). An inn for travelers; especially, an inn belonging to a religious order. (36)

Hroth′gar (hrōth′gär). The king in the story "Beowulf's Fight with Grendel." (226)

hum′bly (hŭm′blĭ). In a humble way; meekly. (202)

hys ter′i cal ly (hĭs tẽr′ĭk lĭ). In a very excited way, as by laughing or crying in an uncontrolled manner; in a wildly emotional way. (76)

I

im mod′er ate ly (ĭm mŏd′ẽr ĭt lĭ). Not moderately; unreasonable; beyond what is usually considered proper or fitting; in an unrestrained way. (160)

Im mor′tal (ĭ môr′tăl). 1. Any god in Greek and Roman mythology. (219) 2. (not capitalized) Not mortal; living or lasting forever.

im pa′la (ĭm pä′là). A large African antelope of a brownish color, with a black crescent-shaped stripe on its hindquarters. (130)

in duce′ (ĭn dūs′). To persuade or influence; to lead on; as, to *induce* a person to buy something. (46)

in her′it (ĭn hẽr′ĭt). 1. To receive by birth; as, to *inherit* a strong body. (320) 2. To come into possession of; as, to *inherit* property.

I′vald (ē′väld). In a Norse myth, the father of some dwarfs who were workers in brass and gold. (242)

J

jaun′ty (jôn′tĭ). Gay and carefree; also, stylish; showy. (121)

jest′er (jĕs′tẽr). 1. A clown; a court fool whose duty was to amuse the king. (254) 2. A person given to joking.

Jester.

Jua ni′ta (hwä nē′tà). The name of a sheep in the story "The River Crossing." (116)

K

Ka′i-al e-al e (kä′ê ä lå ä lå). King of the sharks in the story "The Boy Punia and the King of the Sharks." (210)

Ka rait′ or **krait** (kả rīt′, krīt). A very poisonous snake of India, related to the cobra. (320)

ker′o sene′ (kĕr′ổ sēn′). A thin oil used for burning in lamps and oil stoves. (315)

kin′dle (kĭn′d′l). 1. To set on fire; to light. (215) 2. To arouse; to excite; as, to *kindle* the imagination.

Kru′ger (kroo′gẽr). 1. A national park in the Republic of South Africa. It is a game reserve. (125) 2. Kruger, Stephanus Johannes Paulus, 1825–1904, South African statesman.

L

lad′en (lād′′n). Loaded; burdened; as, a *laden* ship. (75)

la′dle (lā′d′l). 1. A long-handled cuplike spoon used in ladling or dipping. (251) 2. To dip up; as, to *ladle* soup.

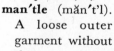

Ladle.

lau′rel (lô′rĕl). A small evergreen tree of southern Europe, having smooth, stiff leaves that were used to make crowns for ancient heroes; also, a bush or tree that is somewhat like the laurel. (84)

lem′ming (lĕm′ĭng). Any of several small rodents having a short tail, furry feet, and small ears. (94)

li′a ble (lī′ả b′l). 1. Likely; especially, unpleasantly likely. (18) 2. Responsible for; bound by law.

li′chen (lī′kĕn). A tiny plant that looks somewhat like moss and that grows flat against rocks or trees. (95)

lim′ber (lĭm′bẽr). 1. To cause to bend or move easily; as, to *limber* up one's arm. (177) 2. Bending easily; as, a *limber* branch.

Lo′ki (lō′kê). In Norse mythology, a god who was a mischief maker and liked to play mean tricks. (240)

lyre (līr). A stringed musical instrument, somewhat like the harp, used by the ancient Greeks. (218)

M

man′tel (măn′t′l). The shelf, beam, or arch above a fireplace. (69)

Mantel.

man′tle (măn′t′l). A loose outer garment without sleeves; a cape. (233)

Mantle.

Man uel′a (män wā′lả). The name of the ranch housekeeper in the story "Spurs for Antonia." (26)

marl′ ditch′ (märl′ dĭch′). A ditch, or trench, from which marl, an earthy deposit, is dug for use as a fertilizer. (187)

mas′sive (măs′ĭv). Big and heavy; large and solid. (105)

---

lāte, alwãys, ăm, ả̆ppear, färm, ȧsk, ả̇lone, câre, wē, ênough, wĕt, silĕnt, lettẽr, hẽre, hīde, hĭd, possĭble, ōld, ổbey, nŏt, cổntrol, hôrse, sổft, ūse, ûnite, ŭs, circŭs, bûrn, mo͞on, fo͝ot, oil, out, that, thin, natụre

maze (māz). 1. A confusing network, as of paths or passages. (94) 2. A state of confusion; as, a *maze* of ideas.

mead (mēd). 1. A fermented drink made of honey and water, with malt, yeast, etc. (229) 2. A meadow.

me′di o′cre (mē′dĭ ō′kẽr). Ordinary; commonplace; not above average. (84)

Menthon, de. See Bernard de Menthon.

midst (mĭdst). The inside or central part or place; middle. (162)

min′a ret′ (mĭn′à rĕt′). A very tall slender tower often attached to a mosque. From one of its balconies the people are called to prayer. (138)

Minaret.

min′strel (mĭn′strĕl). In the Middle Ages, a musical entertainer, especially a singer. (218) 2. One of a group of entertainers. 3. A poet or musician.

Mjol′ ner (myûl′nẽr). In Norse mythology, Thor's hammer. (245)

Mo ham′med an (mō hăm′ĕ dǎn). 1. A follower of Mohammed; a Moslem. (136) 2. Of or having to do with Mohammed or the religion he founded.

Mon′arch y (mŏn′ẽr kĭ). 1. The system of government in which one person, such as a king or queen, is the sole ruler. (44) 2. A country governed by a sole ruler, such as a king.

mon′as ter′y (mŏn′ăs tẽr′ĭ). The building or groups of buildings in which a group of monks or nuns live; a convent. (36)

mon′goose (mŏng′gōōs). A small animal of India that fearlessly attacks and kills poisonous snakes. (313)

mon′ster (mŏn′stẽr). 1. An imaginary or real animal or plant with a strange or horrible form. (226) 2. Any very large animal or thing.

moor (mōōr). 1. An area of open waste land, usually more or less wet. (226) 2. To fasten a boat or ship in place by means of ropes or chains attached to an anchor or the shore.

Mo roc′co (mō rŏk′ō). A country in northern Africa, bordering on the Atlantic Ocean and the western end of the Mediterranean Sea. (136)

mor′tal (môr′tǎl). 1. A being that is subject to death; a human being. (219) 2. Destined to die. 3. Causing death; as, a *mortal* wound.

mosque (mŏsk). A Mohammedan place of public religious worship. (138)

mot′to (mŏt′ō). A short expression that suggests a guiding rule of conduct; as, "Honesty is the best policy." (314)

muf′fler (mŭf′lẽr). 1. A scarf for the neck. (159) 2. Something that deadens noises; as, the *muffler* on an automobile.

N

New Bruns′wick (nū brŭnz′wĭk). A province in the southeastern part of Canada, bordering on the Gulf of St. Lawrence and the Bay of Fundy. (107)

Nils (nĭls). A young boy in "The Wonderful Adventure of Nils." (182)

nurs′er y (nûr′sẽr ĭ). 1. A room set aside for children. (315) 2. A place where young plants, such as trees, are grown.

O

O′din (ō′dĭn). In Norse mythology, the father of the gods. He was god of wisdom, of war, and of poetry. (246)

Or′pheus (ôr′fūs; *commonly* ôr′fē ŭs). In Greek mythology, a poet and musician, the son of Apollo and Calliope. (218)

out (out). In broadcasting, a term meaning to discontinue or end the sound of music or any sound effect. (251)

Ov′id (ŏv′ĭd). 1. The name of a park in the story "The Wonderful Adventure of Nils." (185) 2. A Roman poet.

Ox′en thorpe (ŏk′sĕn thôrp). The name of a road in the story "Tommy Stubbins Meets Doctor Dolittle." (150)

P

par′a pet (păr′á pĕt). 1. A low wall or railing at the edge of a roof, platform, or bridge. (45) 2. A wall of earth or stone to protect soldiers.

Part′let (pärt′lĕt). The name of a hen in the story "Chanticleer and the Fox." (271)

pea′cock′ (pē′kŏk′). A large male bird about the size of a turkey, having beautiful green, gold, and blue feathers. Its tail feathers can be spread out and held upright like a fan. (265)

peal (pēl). 1. A loud sound, or a series of loud sounds, as of bells or thunder. (248) 2. A set of bells; also, the sound of bells.

Pe′ma quid Fort (pĕm′á kwĭd fōrt). A fort in Pemaquid, a small town in southern Maine. (65)

pen in′su la (pĕn ĭn′sŭ lá). A piece of land having water on three sides; also, any piece of land jutting out into the water. (94)

Peninsula.

perch (pûrch). 1. To sit or rest on. (32) 2. A pole or bar put up for birds to roost on. (272) 3. Any high seat or position. 4. A small fresh-water fish.

Per seph′o ne (pẽr sĕf′ó nĕ). In Greek mythology, the wife of Hades and the daughter of Demeter. (220)

Per′sia (pûr′zhá). A country in southwestern Asia, now officially called Iran. (261)

per′son al (pûr′sŭn ăl). 1. Of or about a particular person, or his character, conduct, etc. (196) 2. Of or belonging to a person or persons; not public; private; as, *personal* property.

per suade′ (pẽr swād′). To win to a belief by argument or earnest request; to win over by an appeal. (156)

pet′ti coat (pĕt′ĭ kōt). A skirt worn under a dress. (161)

---

lāte, alwāys, ăm, ȧppear, färm, ȧsk, ȧlone, câre, wē, ênough, wĕt, silĕnt, lettẽr, hēre, hīde, hĭd, possĭble, ōld, ôbey, nŏt, cŏntrol, hôrse, sŏft, ūse, ûnite, ŭs, circŭs, bûrn, mōōn, fŏŏt, oil, out, that, thin, natŭre

pew′ter (pū′tẽr). A metallic substance made of tin, copper, and other metals; also, dishes or other utensils made of pewter. (65)

pil′grim (pĭl′grĭm). 1. A person who travels to a holy place or shrine as an act of religious devotion. (36) 2. A wanderer; a traveler.

pol lute′ (pŏ lūt′). To soil; to make impure; as, to *pollute* drinking water. (97)

pon′der ous (pŏn′dẽr ŭs). 1. Heavy and clumsy. (64) 2. Of great weight. 3. Tiresome; dull.

prat′tle (prat″l). 1. To talk freely and carelessly. (275) 2. To talk a great deal without much meaning; to chatter. 3. Trifling or childish talk.

pre dic′tion (prĕ dĭk′shŭn). Something told or declared beforehand; foretold. (142)

prey (prā). 1. To hunt, seize, or devour anything; as, cats *prey* on mice. (95) 2. Any animal hunted or killed by another animal for food.

priv′i lege (prĭv′ĭ lĭj). 1. A right or liberty granted to a person; a favor. (221) 2. To grant a special right or liberty to someone.

pros′per (prŏs′pẽr). To succeed; to turn out well; to thrive. (275)

prov′i dence (prŏv′ĭ dĕns). 1. A divine .act of help or care. (321) 2. (capitalized) God; Loving Father of all human beings.

pro vi′sion (prŏ vĭzh′ŭn). 1. A stock or store of food; as, to have plenty of *provisions*. (151) 2. Act of providing or supplying; as, the *provision* of tents for a camping trip.

prowl (proul). 1. To move about in a quiet and secret way like a wild animal hunting for food. (127) 2. To wander about.

Pu-ni′ a (pōō nē′ä). The name of the boy who got the better of the sharks in the story "The Boy Pu-nia and the King of the Sharks." (210)

pu′ny (pū′nĭ). Weak; of less than usual size and strength; as, a *puny* cat. (16)

Q

quar′ry (kwŏr′ĭ). 1. A hunted animal or bird; game; prey. (88) 2. A place where building stone is dug, cut, or blasted.

quill (kwĭl). 1. A spine of the hedgehog or porcupine. (103) 2. A large stiff feather.

R

Ram′a dan′ (răm′*a* dän′). In the Mohammedan year, the ninth month when strict fasting is practiced from dawn to sunset; also, the fasting. (136)

Ra mon′ (rä môn′). The name of an old man who tended sheep in the story "The River Crossing." (112)

ra′tion (rāsh′ŭn). 1. A fixed allowance or allotment, as of food. (139) 2. To fix or limit, by law or official order, the amounts of something, as food or clothing, that can be bought by a person at one time.

ra′ven (rā′vĕn). 1. A glossy-black bird, somewhat like a large crow, found in the northern regions of the world. (196) 2. A deep, shiny black.

Raven.

reg′is ter (rĕj′ĭs tẽr). 1. To enroll; to enter in a list. (125) 2. A written record of regular entries; a book for such a record; as, a school *register*. 3. Something that records; as, a cash *register*.

re sem′ble (rē zĕm′b'l). To be like in appearance or quality; to be similar to. (141)

re serve′ (rē zûrv′). 1. Land set aside for a particular purpose; as, a forest *reserve*. (125) 2. To have set aside or held for one's use; as, to *reserve* a room in a hotel.

rhi noc′er os (rī nŏs′ẽr ŏs). A large, thick-skinned animal of Asia and Africa. It has one or two heavy, upright horns on the snout. (125)

Rik′ki-tik′ki-ta′vi (rĭk′ĭ tĭk′ĭ tä′vĭ). The name of the mongoose in the story "Rikki-tikki-tavi" which is from the *Jungle Book* by Rudyard Kipling. (312)

ro′dent (rō′dĕnt). One of several small animals that have long, sharp front teeth used for gnawing. A rat is a rodent. (94)

Ro me′ro (rō mā′rō). The name of the ranch foreman in the story "Spurs for Antonia." (26)

S

sac′ri fice (săk′rĭ fīs). 1. The giving up of one thing for another; especially, an unselfish giving up. (36) 2. The act of making an offering to God or to a god. 3. Something that is offered up as a religious act. 4. Loss; as, sell the house at a *sacrifice*.

San′cho (sän′chō). The name of a dog in the story "The River Crossing." (117)

sap′phire (săf′īr). 1. A bright, clear blue. (128) 2. A transparent, bright-blue precious stone.

scut′tle (skŭt′l). 1. To run hurriedly from view; to scamper. (313) 2. To cut a hole in a boat with the intention of sinking it. 3. A short, swift run. 4. A type of bucket.

Se gow′lee (sŭ gou′lē). The name of a cantonment in India, in the story "Rikki-tikki-tavi." (313)

sen′try (sĕn′trĭ). A person, especially a soldier, standing guard. (250)

set′tle (sĕt′l). A wooden bench with arms and a high solid back. (75)

Settle.

sheathe (shēth). To put a knife or sword into its case or sheath. (142)

shorn (shōrn). A past participle of shear (shẽr), meaning to cut off; to clip; to shave. (241)

Sif (sĭf). In Norse mythology, a goddess with beautiful golden hair. She was the wife of Thor; guardian of the home. (240)

Si′gnor (sē′nyôr). Sir; Mr. An Italian word used before a man's name as a title of address or respect. (136)

---

lāte, alwãys, ăm, ȧppear, färm, ȧsk, ȧlone, câre, wē, ênough, wĕt, silĕnt, lettẽr, hẽre, hīde, hĭd, possĭble, ōld, ôbey, nŏt, cŏntrol, hôrse, sŏft, ūse, ûnite, ŭs, circŭs, bûrn, mōōn, fŏŏt, oil, out, that, thin, natŭre

Sind′re (sĭn′drĕ). In Norse mythology, the name of a dwarf who was a very clever worker in metals. (243)

singe (sĭnj). 1. To burn the ends or outside of. (326) 2. A slight burn.

Sir′le (sûr′lē). The name of a squirrel in "The Wonderful Adventure of Nils." (187)

site (sīt). The place where something was, is, or is to be; as, a good *site* for a camp. (38)

Skid′blad ner (skĭd′blȧd nĕr). In Norse mythology, the name of a ship that always found a breeze to drive it wherever its master would go. (243)

slough (slōō). A marshy place; a swamp; also, a tide flat. (158)

Smir′re (smẽr′rē). The name of a fox in "The Wonderful Adventure of Nils." (190)

snag (snăg). 1. To catch on something; as, to *snag* one's coat on a branch. (177) 2. A rough, projecting part; a stump; especially, a stump in a lake or river. 3. An unexpected difficulty; as, to meet a *snag* in one's work.

sor′rel (sŏr′ĕl). 1. A horse of a yellowish-brown or reddish-brown color. (31) 2. A yellowish-brown or reddish brown color.

sou′ve nir′ (sōō′vĕ nẽr′). Something which serves as a reminder; a keepsake. (48)

spig′ot (spĭg′ŭt). 1. A faucet. (54) 2. A peg used to stop the hole in a cask, or barrel.

Spigot.

sprat (sprăt). A kind of small herring. (251)

stock ade′ (stŏk ād′). 1. A line of strong posts set in the ground for a barrier or defense. (70) 2. A pen or enclosure made of posts and stakes.

strive (strīv). 1. To try hard; to make an effort. (220) 2. To fight; to struggle against, with, or for, something.

suc ces′sion (sŭk sĕsh′ŭn). 1. A series of persons or things that follow one after another. (104) 2. The order, act, or right of taking possession of or succeeding to an office, throne, title, or property. 3. A series; as, a *succession* of accidents.

sul′tan (sŭl′tăn). A ruler or sovereign of a Mohammedan state. (136)

sur vey′or (sẽr vā′ẽr). A person whose work is finding out and making a record of the outline, measurements, and position of a piece of land, a road, etc. (162)

swamp (swŏmp). Wet, spongy land; a marsh. (229)

T

Tai′na ron (tâ′nä rôn). In Greek mythology, the name of a cavern which led to the World of the Dead. (219)

tal′on (tăl′ŭn). The claw of an animal; especially, the claw of a bird of prey, such as a hawk or an eagle. (95)

tan′ta lize (tăn′tȧ līz). To tease by withholding something desirable. (160)

tar pau′lin (tär pô′lĭn). A very heavy cloth, such as canvas, which is waterproof, and used especially on ships to cover hatches, hammocks, etc. (56)

thong (thŏng). A strap or strip of leather, especially one used for fastening something. (18)

Thong.

Thor (thôr). In Norse mythology, the god of thunder. He was also a god of strength, a helper in war. (240)

throng (thrŏng). 1. To crowd together; to move, pass, or go in great numbers. (102) 2. A large gathering.

Thumb′ ie tot′ (thŭm′ bĭ tŏt′). A name given to Nils meaning Tom Thumb. (190)

tit′mice′ (tĭt′mīs′). Plural of tit′-mouse′ (tĭt′mous′), a small, insect-eating bird, with soft plumage, gray, black, or white in color. (187)

tor′rent (tŏr′ĕnt). 1. A downpour; as, a *torrent* of rain. (152) 2. A rushing stream, as of water or lava.

trace (trās). 1. A mark left by a person or thing, such as a track or a footprint. (259) 2. A very small amount; as, a *trace* of color in the sky. 3. To follow or track the course of; as, to *trace* a fox to its den.

trans form′ (trăns fôrm′). To change in form or nature; as, a caterpillar is *transformed* into a butterfly. (185)

Trans vaal′ (trăns väl′). A province in the northeastern part of the Republic of South Africa. (125)

trea′cle (trē′k'l). Molasses; especially, molasses which drains from sugar-refining molds. (201)

tro′phy (trō′fĭ). Any memorial of a victory or conquest; as, a golf *trophy*. (237)

trough (trŏf). 1. A long, narrow channel or hollow between waves. (56) 2. A kind of large, open box, long and shallow, especially one used to hold water or food for cattle or other animals. (80)

tuft (tŭft). 1. A small cluster, as one of hairs, threads, feathers, or blades of grass, fastened at one end. (317) 2. A clump of bushes or trees.

tur′ret ed (tûr′ĕt ĕd). 1. Shaped like a turret or tower. (271) 2. Furnished with a turret or turrets which are small towers, often on the corner of the building.

U

up (ŭp). In broadcasting, a term meaning to increase, or swell, the sound of music or of any sound effects. (251)

Up′sal quitch (ŭp′săl kwĭch). A river in the northern part of New Brunswick, Canada. (102)

V

va′cant (vā′kănt). Without a person to hold it or occupy it; empty; not put to use; idle. (171)

vac′ci na′tion (văk′sĭ nā′shŭn). The act of vaccinating, or inoculating, a person or an animal with something that will prevent or lessen the power of a certain disease. (27)

---

lāte, alwāys, ăm, ăppear, färm, àsk, alone, câre, wē, ênough, wĕt, silĕnt, lettĕr, hĕre, hīde, hĭd, possĭble, ōld, ôbey, nŏt, cŏntrol, hôrse, sŏft, ūse, ûnite, ŭs, circŭs, bûrn, mōon, fŏŏt, oil, out, that, thin, natŭre

val′iant (văl′yănt). 1. Boldly brave; courageous; stouthearted. (327) 2. Done bravely; heroic; as, a *valiant* deed.

va ri′e ty (vȧ rī′ĕ tĭ). 1. A number of different kinds. (125) 2. A particular kind; as, a new *variety* of apple.

vat (văt). A large container for liquids; a large tank or barrel. (251)

ven′ture (vĕn′tŭr). 1. To dare to make or give an opinion. (68) 2. To undertake the risk of; to dare. (86) 3. An undertaking in which there is risk; as, a business *venture*.

ve ran′da (vĕ răn′dȧ). A porch; especially, a long, roofed porch along the side or sides of a house. (315)

Veranda.

ver mil′ion (vĕr mĭl′yŭn). 1. Any of a number of bright red colors. (69) 2. The bright red coloring matter.

verse (vûrs). 1. A stanza or group of lines of poetry. (200) 2. A single line

of poetry. 3. One of the short divisions of a chapter in the Bible.

Vi′king (vī′kĭng). One of the pirate Northmen who plundered the coasts of Europe in the 8th, 9th, and 10th centuries. (240)

W

ward′er (wôr′dĕr). A person who keeps guard; a watchman; a warden; a jailer. (44)

wa′ter hy′a cinth (wô′tĕr hī′ȧ sĭnth). A tropical plant that grows in a pool or pond. It is a plant of the lily family with spikes of fragrant, bell-shaped flowers. (132)

whence (hwĕns). From what place, person, or source. (228)

whit′tle (hwĭt′'l). To pare or cut off chips from wood; to carve, shape, or form by paring or cutting. (160)

Y

year′ling (yẽr′lĭng). A child, animal, or plant that is a year old. (28)

BCDEFGHIJ069876543

PRINTED IN THE UNITED STATES OF AMERICA